"In *Jordi*, Dr. Rubin may well answer Louis Untermeyer's question, 'But who shall fathom the mind of a child?' The author is a practicing psychiatrist in Brooklyn, N. Y. The mind fathomed is a psychotic one. In the pages of this little book, neither case study nor narrative, the response is revelatory and provocative, unsentimental and deeply moving."

Lisa and David: "A triumphant and authentic pattern of the slow return toward health made by two mentally ill adolescents. David is brilliant and bitter, obsessed by the necessity for painful cleanliness, safe only with reliable clock mechanisms, convinced that a touch from another human can bring death. Lisa-Muriel is divided into two desperate entities, talks only in nonsense rhyme and must jump and skip ceaselessly to discharge her driving energy. Both are terrified in the sick cages they have built for themselves away from the world and equally terrified of leaving them, and as they haltingly grope forth in an awareness of each other we know them as touchingly intrepid."—from the reviews of Dr. Rubin's books in *The Washington Post*

BOOKS BY THEODORE ISAAC RUBIN

Jordi
Lisa and David
In the Life

THEODORE ISAAC RUBIN

JORDI LISA & DAVID

"*Alone, alone, all, all alone;/Alone on a wide, wide sea.*"
(*Ancient Mariner*, Samuel T. Coleridge)

BALLANTINE BOOKS   NEW YORK

BALLANTINE BOOKS, INC.
101 Fifth Avenue, New York 3, N. Y.

Contents

Preface

There is no "Jordi." But in my work I have come to know Jordi's of all ages. I thank them for so many things. They inspired this book, indeed helped compose it. They enhanced my growth, both professionally and personally, and above all they have allowed me to share their experiences. Together we've made some wonderful voyages from darkness to light.

I have endeavored to write a book which is scientifically correct. However, the main endeavor of the book is to convey the feeling, panic, suffering, and tragedy involved in mental disturbance and more explicitly in childhood schizophrenia. Disturbances of this nature are, at best, poorly understood illnesses.

There is a new trend in psychiatry, the establishment of day hospitals, day centers, and day schools for seriously disturbed people. I feel this is a warm, human, healthy approach to a most difficult problem. I would like to congratulate Dr. Carl Fenichel, director and founder of the "League School for Seriously Disturbed Children." Carl Fenichel is indeed a pioneer, engaged in a noble constructive task. His effort will shed much light on this important new apporach to the management of very disturbed children.

A special thanks to Florence Stiller—a warm human being—a great friend. Her encouragement, criticism, and "being there" helped me every inch of the way.

Thanks to Nat Freeman, who made it all possible; my wife, Ellie, for both inspiration and technical assistance; and my children, Trudy and Jeff, for helping me to understand other children.

Jordi

For Ellie

The End

⚭

He ran through the train yelling wildly, and nobody heard him. He was alone in the crowded subway and felt that he had to get to the first car before the next station. He tried squeezing between people's legs, but they didn't budge. Much as he struggled, he went unnoticed.

He sat up in bed. The room was dark, and he had to get to the front of the train. Quickly he put on his shirt and trousers and ran quietly out of the house to the IRT. He had several tokens from previous trips. With some difficulty he pushed through the turnstile and was surprised to see nobody on the plat-form. Funny, how crowded the station and train could be one minute and empty the next—but this didn't bother him.

He rode from Flatbush Avenue to Van Cortlandt Park—standing in front and watching each station's light and warmth reach out to him through the black-ness of the tunnel. He knew the stations by heart. They were really old friends—the only friends he ever had.

On the trip back, he fell asleep, leaning against the glass of number one car again.

At Flatbush Avenue the conductor shook him and

asked, "What in the world are you doing on the train four o'clock in the morning?"

He pulled away from the big man and ran out of the train, screaming and crying. In no time at all he was home again and in bed.

∞

He woke up suddenly, looked around the room, and jumped out of bed. People were talking in the kitchen. The woman's voice was high-pitched, tremulous, and sounded very angry. The man's voice said, "Yes—OK, already, OK," and then the door slammed and it was quiet again. He felt like eating but was afraid to go into the kitchen. The garbage pail under the sink, with its greasy, gaping, smelly hole frightened him awfully.

Shaking miserably, he finally opened the door and walked into the room backward. The woman shook her head and said, "Why can't you walk like all of us, Jordi?" He couldn't answer—the pail might hear him. The big hole was like an ear, and it could hear everything—sometimes even his thoughts. If he kept quiet and thought nothing, maybe he could shut it out and make himself safe.

He gulped down his orange juice and ran out of the house. He made it—he was safe again—but he had to be careful of the garbage pails on the street.

And then he remembered that he forgot his jiggler. He had to have his jiggler if he wanted to get by the garbage cans safely. He knew that he had to face the woman again. She just couldn't understand why he wouldn't talk. Sometimes she hugged and kissed him. Sometimes she gave up and shook him.

He marveled at her fearlessness. She talked in front of the can, even picked it up and shook it. But her voice—when that voice got loud and angry, the whole room shook. It felt like he would be crushed by it. It went through him and made him shake and scream inside—stop, stop, stop, stop, stop, but her voice would go on. Sometimes, though, the man's voice, which was kind and deep and smooth, would say, "Stop," and her voice stopped.

He tiptoed into the house, but she saw him and said, "God, Jordi, walk like the rest of us." He took the doorknob attached to a long string and ran past her out of the house. He had his jiggler and was now truly safe.

He let the jiggler hang down in front of him and waited. Soon it would tell his feet where to go. Funny, how his feet followed the jiggler without his even thinking about them. He walked and walked and felt that he was all alone even though there were people here and there.

His feet finally came to the jiggler's destination. There it was—a water tower, very high—sitting up there in the clouds, alone and quiet. He looked at the tower, and it made him feel good inside. He stared at it for a long time, and then the jiggler reminded him that he had to go home again.

All the way home he thought of water towers, flag-poles, high buildings, trees, and many things much taller than he was. Before he knew it, he and his jiggler were in the kitchen eating lunch. Her voice asked if he had a nice walk, and he nodded yes. She kissed the top of his head lovingly, and he said, "It was high—so high, so beautiful."

"What was high? What, Jordi?"

But he was quiet and didn't feel like talking again.

13

It rained that morning. He liked the lightning, and the thunder was rumbly and warm. It was the rain that scared him. Every time it came, the same thought was there—rain forest—and it would repeat over and over again—rain forest, rain forest—and the same picture popped into his head—only lately he was more and more in the picture.

The trees were raining down. They weren't the tall, nice ones. They were short, fat, heavy, and stubby. They had giant roots—that spread out all over. And they came down from the sky to look for him, and one day one would come—the one that hated him most. It would crush him into the dirt. The roots would strangle him. He would be buried deeper and deeper.

Jordi jumped out of bed screaming, "Let me go, let me go! I'm choking, choking!" He was out of the house now—in the street, lying on his back—he clawed the air, gasping for breath.

The neighbor from next door said, "The kid is having a fit." Jordi didn't hear her—the trees were raining down.

∞

The days and nights passed. There were the quiet, safe times—the withdrawn hours. And there were the terrors, the seconds of panic. Sometimes they stretched out into hours, and even days.

He walked out of the house dangling his jiggler before him. He waited for directions. Three boys passed him. They were bored. One said, "Let's have some fun with that queer-looking kid."

One of the other boys grabbed the jiggler and began to swing it around in a wide arc.

Jordi was frozen to the spot. A piece was torn out of his middle. He watched the jiggler go round and round. He felt his head whirl. He didn't even feel the other two boys pushing him. He didn't hear their taunting words. His agony was too great.

And then he began to scream. He didn't hear his own voice. He screamed and screamed and paused only to gasp for breath.

The boy dropped the jiggler and ran, and the other two followed. Jordi's mother ran down the stairs, hugged him to her, and picked up the jiggler. They walked upstairs with his head pressed against her belly.

He couldn't stop moaning. The gaping wound was still there. She put him in his bed, washed his face, kissed him and hugged him. After she placed the jiggler in his hand, he fell asleep, exhausted.

He listened to them talking and knew that it was all about him. He was curious but not really interested.

The sounds, and the feelings that they conveyed, moved him somewhere deep inside. The words, however, were just nothing.

The woman's voice was full of tears. "What shall we do, Dan? Where? What school? None will have him. . . . I love that kid so, Dan. He's so helpless. . . . Where did we hurt him? How?"

Jordi lost interest and fell asleep. He was part of his dream now and could not hear his father weeping. He was on a train, all alone. He came to many stations full of light and high towers. There were no people, noise, or garbage cans. He slept soundly.

∞

The sunlight woke him. The same mean trick had been played on him again. From his very own world he was plunged again into this hated place; people, garbage cans—big ones, little ones. If he could only remain as when his eyes were closed all day like at night—but they all had a way of getting close to him.

And he couldn't shut them out. There were times when he ran and ran, and there were times when he swung his jiggler furiously—but they were still there. Their voices were all around him. And sometimes the voices were there by themselves. And they yelled at him, chided him, prodded him, and he was afraid—he was so afraid—and there was no place to go, no one he could trust.

Irene and Dan visited the state institution. They knew there was no choice, but they couldn't bring themselves to commit him. The place looked so forbidding, they felt so hopeless. Their little boy, their first born, Jordi in Brooksville. They tore at themselves and at each other. But the grim fact stuck. No other place would have him.

And then the letter arrived. Mrs. Harris, the last of a multitude of psychiatric social workers they had consulted, informed them that a special school had been organized. She warned them, however, not to be too optimistic. The school would accept only a handful of children—and these only after much testing, interviewing, and screening. The principal prerequisite had to be fulfilled. In order to be admitted a child had to be severely disturbed—in fact, psychotic.

Jordi was observed for hours. There were rooms with one-way mirrors and interviews and tests of all kinds. He played with blocks, ink blots, and little statues of children and adults. The doctors examined him physically as well as mentally. The final diagnostic summary of tests, reports, and interviews read as follows:

"This eight-year-old white, sandy-haired, blue-eyed boy is slightly smaller than his stated age would indicate. ENT are normal. Chest is clear, and heart and circulatory system are normal. Neurological examination is negative. Complete physical examination reveals no system pathology or evidence of organic defect of any kind.

"This child is only moderately oriented in time,

place, and person. He apparently suffers from severe anxiety—panic attacks, hallucinatory phenomena—and at times is autistic. Contact is possible but tenuous. There is an obvious thought disorder in evidence. Although there is at times severe intellectual blocking, there is nevertheless evidence of a superior I.Q. and good intellectual potential. The opinion of the diagnostic staff is that this child is suffering from a severe psychotic reaction, undoubtably schizophrenic in nature.

"Final diagnosis: Schizophrenic reaction—type: mixed, undifferentiated, chronic."

Jordi had passed the entrance examination. He was admitted to the school.

The Middle

∞

They led him out of the house into the bus. It was very different from the trains and their routes that he knew so well. Then they went out of the familiar neighborhood.

He was afraid to sit, and nobody objected to his standing the whole way. He felt very small. It made him feel a little bit bigger to stand. He kept his fist clenched tightly on the seat, and his body became more rigid. As familiar surroundings disappeared, he clenched the seat even tighter, feeling that this would keep him from disappearing too.

He felt that if he held himself tightly and didn't budge, he would not come apart. It took immense concentration to hold himself together. Each bump and jolt threatened to make him scatter into little pieces. A private battle was taking place between him and the lurching of the bus.

The attendant talked to him. He didn't answer. He couldn't hear her. Keeping himself in one part absorbed him totally. All of his senses were concentrated on the terrible effort.

He was aware that they were no longer moving. The scene outside the window was a new one. He did not want to step into this scene. The handle of his seat in the bus was his grip on himself. He couldn't let go—he would surely lose himself.

He heard them reasoning and pleading, but he felt that theirs were foreign voices. He couldn't understand their strange language. If they could only go back—back so that he and his jiggler could become themselves again. And then he knew he was saved. He remembered his jiggler. He reached in his pocket and squeezed it.

Friend, friend—lovely, lovely jiggler, he thought.

He felt the strength and wholeness return to him. The jiggler chased the shakiness right out of him.

He was still afraid, but he squeezed the jiggler and felt connected to the old scene. He walked off the bus. The jiggler felt like it hooked the new scene to the old one. He told himself that this was just a part of the places he knew—not a new place—really a newer part of the old place. That way he wasn't new either. That way he remained himself—Jordi.

But when he saw the building, his stomach felt funny. He wasn't so sure now. Holding his jiggler tighter made him feel better. Then he realized he knew the building. This was the place where he fooled with the ink people. Only this time she wasn't there. She stayed at home. He remembered the doctor listening to his chest. He couldn't go in. He trembled. He wanted to run. The streets, crisscrossing wherever he looked, were like a big puzzle he could get caught in. The bus—the bus—the bus. Where was it? Where, where? He charged into it and shrank into the back seat. He clutched the jiggler so tightly his hand became numb. And then he knew he was dying.

He thought, dead, dead—spread—spread. They fit together. And so it was so. He would soon be dead. Spread—dead—dead spread, he thought. He waited for it to happen. He felt his arm become numb, but he was no longer jumpy. The deadness also brought calmness. The panic was gone, and he waited to die.

But then they were in the bus talking to him. He paid no attention. Dying occupied him completely. Then he realized that they were gone. But now a tray of food was on the next seat, and he forgot to die. He was too busy eating, and the bus felt good. After all, it was connected to the old place.

Now and then he saw a stranger come in. But no words were spoken.

After a while the bus was full again, and in motion. This time he sat comfortably the whole trip. The bus felt warmer—kind of cozy and safe.

He looked around and watched the strangers. He held his jiggler all the time but didn't take it out of his pocket.

He noticed the stranger next to him. Then he looked at the one next to that one. After he looked at them all, he felt a little bit better. But he still wanted to stop being with them. They were still strangers.

He concentrated on the big man behind the wheel. He remembered the man on the train. Only this man sat; the others walked up and down.

Then he saw the water tower—his very own water tower. There it was, out the window. He got up and ran to that side of the bus. At the same time he yelled, "Hi, tower, high tower—my tower."

In no time at all the bus was parked in front of his house. He jumped out eagerly. She was there to hold him and hug him.

He looked around. Nothing had changed.

He was home from his first day at school.

He drank his milk slowly, watching her as she did the dishes.

Then she asked, "How was it, Jordi?"

"The man was the same on the train."

"What man?"

"The man who sat."

"Who sat, Jordi?"

"The big stranger."

"But how was school, Jordi?"

"School, pool, fool, tool. So jiggle, jiggle."

He took the jiggler out of his pocket and left the house.

The sun was going down, and he felt cold. He went back to the house and put on his sweater. Then he dangled the jiggler and waited.

The jiggler took him all over the neighborhood. He checked all the places—the tower, the busy street, the subway station. All of it was like before.

Then it was dark, and he felt the jiggler lead him home.

After supper he was very tired. He went to his room and soon fell asleep.

He dreamed that he went to his stations, but, instead of a train, he was on a bus. It was warm and nice. And the stations were nice too. And the big sitting man wasn't a stranger. But then they came to a big empty building. He looked inside and could see it was cold. He heard her say, "Jordi—Jordi, school, school," and sat up fully awake.

He waited for the bus full of strangers to arrive. He heard her voice go up and down. It felt good hearing it close to him that way. But he paid no attention to what it said.

He picked up the dried-out leaf and examined it carefully. Then he traced the veins and their branches between his thumb and forefinger. After a while he rolled it into a ball and crushed it, watching the powder blow away before it reached the ground. Then he picked up a green leaf and tried the same thing. But it turned into a green mash, and his fingers got sticky with its juice. When he licked them, he was surprised at the bitter taste and made a funny face. He heard her voice say, "What's the matter, Jordi?"

And he said, "Nothing, just leaf fingers."

Then the bus arrived, and this time he went in and sat down.

He felt funny with the strangers, and his stomach felt uneasy when the bus left the old neighborhood. Then he recognized a few of the faces. When he saw the same man driving, he thought, train man, and the bad feeling left.

He looked out of the window. It felt as though the streets were rushing by him as he sat still. Then he thought of them as flat boats, and the road became an ocean. Their decks carried many interesting objects, all passing by so he could see them. He felt very important and watched the passing boats carefully. There were all kinds and sizes of people. There were carriages. Then he saw a black cat, and he turned it into a panther. The bus carried him away from the scene just as the panther was about to eat up one of the children.

He felt kind of filled up, puffed out, and lifted. Then suddenly the importance just poured out. It was as though a hole had been punched in the middle of him. The stuff just bled out, and he could feel himself shrinking. And then he felt small, and weak and scared again. They had stopped, and there it was. The big red ink building. He felt the coldness of the doctor's stethoscope again, and knew that it was cold inside.

He watched them all leave the bus. Even the train man left. Then he saw them go into the building. He sat and watched and wondered if they would be frozen by the coldness inside. Then he thought of the building—an ice building, all ice inside.

He thought of ice cubes, and his mother cracking them. He pictured the people walking around in there, cold and stiff. Then he thought of them bumping into each other, and pieces cracking off them like ice cubes.

But then he saw the train man leave the building. He watched him walk down the street. He was surprised to see that he walked quickly and softly, without being stiff at all.

Then he saw somebody look out the doorway at him. He quickly turned his head to the other side, but she didn't look stiff either—even soft. He looked back. No—she really didn't look frozen. Then she disappeared inside.

He took his jiggler out, and let it hang between his legs. It pointed to the door. He followed it. He kept following it. Then he looked up and realized he was out of the bus. He was in the new scene. First he wanted to run back to the bus. But then the sun came from behind a cloud, and the street looked bright and warm like other streets he knew.

He walked around the block several times. When he passed the ice house, a stranger waved to him from the window—but he didn't wave back.

The jiggler took him all over the block. Then he walked through the adjoining streets. He looked at the brownstone houses, and they seemed old and tired to him. Then he came to a busy street—full of stores, traffic, and people. For a while he watched a man wash the windows of a five-and-dime store. Then he walked on and came to an IRT subway station. He went down the stairs, looked the platform over, and then came back into the sunlight.

He covered the whole area three times. Then he went back to the ice house. Now the streets were not so new, and he felt better. But the bus was gone. He looked up and down the street—but no bus. He began to feel very frightened. Then he thought of the subway station two blocks away and felt the shakiness stop.

Then the lady stranger brought a sandwich and milk out to him. She sat near him on the stoop, but he paid no attention to her. He just ate his lunch and thought about the subway station.

And then the rain started. He pictured the rain trees and shuddered. This time he heard her when she said, "Come in, Jordi. Come in out of the rain."

He was afraid to walk any farther. He leaned against the wall and thought, it isn't an ice house; it isn't. It isn't an ice house; it isn't, it isn't an ice house.

But he couldn't go in. Then the girl came into the hall and said, "Come. Come with Lisa—Lisa—Muriel. Come, come."

He stared at her but didn't budge.

Then she said, "Aw, come on; come on, kid. John, the kid won't come. He won't come, ho hum—ho hum, the kid won't come."

The rhyme interested him. He muttered, "Ho hum, ho hum—won't come, won't come."

She lost interest, though, and disappeared into the room. Forgetting his inhibitions, he walked through the hall to the edge of the room. He could see the whole room now but stopped short. He wanted to go in but just couldn't. Then he began to rock up and back from foot to foot—left to right, right to left. It was almost as if he had to dissipate the energy of his indecision by means of this constant to-and-fro rocking.

The room was very big, with lots of windows and lights. There were all kinds of colored pictures on the walls and a great big blackboard on one side. Then he saw an open closet and all kinds of toys and game boxes sticking out. In the center of the room was a big table with pencils, papers, and crayons on it. Along one side there were several low tables. There were little and big strangers here and there. One stranger looked at him the whole time. And then he remembered her—she was the same one who looked at him through the window when he walked around the block.

Then the Lisa–Muriel girl stranger came over to him again.

"Come in, kid, come in.

"John," she yelled to her teacher. "John."

A big man stranger came over. "Yes, Lisa, what is it?"

"This kid, this iddy bid kid, won't come in."

"He will when he's ready to, Lisa. When he's ready, he'll come in with his teacher."

"Who's his teacher, John, who? Not you, John, not you."

"Not me, Lisa. Sally is his teacher—Sally over there," he said, pointing at the woman still standing close to Jordi.

Teacher, teacher, Jordi thought. Teacher stranger—strangers, the public—a public, stranger teacher.

He looked at the woman a second but then got interested in Lisa again. But she no longer knew he was there. She was busy now, alternately hopping and skipping around the room. Periodically she let out a whoop and said, "Muriel, Muriel isn't my name, but to me it's the same, the same, the same."

Then a funny thing happened. He saw a picture of the Eiffel Tower on the adjacent wall. He ran over to it and into the room and yelled, "A tower, a tower!"

The woman stranger—the Sally one—sat down in a chair next to him while he looked at the travel poster hanging on the wall.

∞

The smell of the place was strong and clean. It felt exciting and new. But the unfamiliarity made him feel funny in his stomach. It was like breathing something other than air—heady, strange, and somewhat frightening.

She seemed that way to him too. She was new and fresh, but different. She did the same thing day after day. She met him at the bus, walked inside with him, and was there. Wherever he went, she was there. Whatever he did, she was there. For a long time they said nothing to each other and never touched each other. But—no matter what—there she was, close to him. They were inseparable from the time he got off the bus in the morning until he left for home in the late afternoon. After a while he couldn't shut her out.

After a long time, a change took place. This change was subtle and slow. Jordi was not aware of its happening. But their relationship had changed. He no longer felt that she was separate from him. She and he were one. They had merged—the boundaries of their separate skins were no longer a barrier. And yet a thin line separated the her part of him from the rest of him. Her, she—that part was different; it was with different feelings—warm and soft—but very solid.

And then they began to talk.

⦾

At first their conversation was limited to one or two words.

She would say hello, and he would reply with a timid hello.

And after a while they called each other by name. He kind of liked the name Sally.

And gradually their talking became more complicated. There were more words, and with the words more understanding and feeling passed between them.

⦾

He couldn't stand the new feeling. It got stronger and stronger and then would leave. When it was gone, he felt nothing—just flat. But the feeling would come again, and he felt torn apart from inside by it. He walked on the street near the school with her. The feeling hit—his heart beat wildly. He grabbed her hand.

"Sally. Sally, garbage cans—cans, cans. Sally, please—over again. Ears, ears—hear me—hear me. Cans—please—please."

She walked to the can in front of the school. She kicked it savagely; her face was contorted with anger. She stomped it—and cursed it—and held his hand all the time.

"Hit it, Jordi. Hit it—kick it. Kick it—come on, Jordi. That god-damned can—let's kill it, Jordi."

Jordi felt his head exploding. He jumped on the can —he screamed wildly—he stamped up and down. The can was almost completely flat—there was no hole left. He stopped yelling—calmed down. There was no new feeling now—and no flat one either.

"Sally. Sally, no can—no can—no ear. It's gone. I made it go—I made it go."

"You were angry, Jordi—angry, angry. Remember, Jordi, you were angry."

Jordi muttered to himself, "Angry, angry. I was angry."

The word was familiar—but now the symbol, the meaning, and the feeling were closer to being one. Jordi played with the word for days—tasted it, chewed it up, tested it. "Angry, angry. Sally—I was angry."

⚭

She hit him with her fist. Then she pulled his shirt and kicked his ankle. She yelled in a high-pitched voice, "Louse, louse, leave Lisa alone, alone. Lisa wants to go home now. Lisa wants the crayons—louse, louse."

She kicked his ankle again and again.

Jordi couldn't move. He repeated, "Louse, louse," and then his body began to shake while he slumped down to the floor. His ankle hurt, and he felt bruised and miserable. Sally yanked him to his feet.

"Lisa is hitting John, not you, Jordi. John, John. John is John. Jordi is Jordi."

"My foot—my foot," Jordi wept.

"Jordi, *your* foot. The foot of Jordi—you—Jordi. Your foot is fine.

"John—John over there with Lisa—his foot hurts—not your foot. John's foot. Jordi is Jordi. John is John."

"Jordi is Jordi—Jordi is Jordi. I'm Jordi."

Jordi felt his ankle, then his shirt. He looked at John and Lisa. Lisa's teacher—John—talked to her in a low voice. He heard the word "crayon" repeated.

"I'm Jordi—my ankle is fine. Sally, I'm me—Sally, I'm me. John is the louse. Lisa says John is the louse."

"Yes, Jordi, yes. Lisa means John, not you."

"What is a louse, Sally?"

The bus wound its way through a narrow residential street and then made a right turn on Ocean Avenue. It rattled along pleasantly—its age in quaint contrast to the modern surroundings in which it found itself. Both sides of the broad avenue were lined with tall concrete and brick buildings. Here and there a one-family house interposed itself among the massive structures.

The small houses and the bus were from an age gone by, a safer, slower time—not as efficient or comfortable perhaps, but not as slick, cold, and imposing either.

Jordi was aware of it all, even though he formulated

none of it in words. He was simply aware of his feeling that the bus was warm and homelike—as were the little houses. The tall buildings intrigued him, reaching for the clouds as they did, but the mass of them, connected to one another on both sides of the street, formed a frightening gauntlet for the little bus to run through.

He looked through the back window and shivered happily. His mind's eye viewed a terrible scene indeed. From both sides buildings were crashing down to fill and obliterate Ocean Avenue. Only the bus and the occasional small houses remained intact.

The small bus miraculously escaped the ever-encroaching wave of destruction left in its wake. Huge pieces of buildings—bricks, glass, and cement boulders—smashed against the back of it. They were reduced to small particles and dust clouds. The bus was simply impervious to the explosive crashing destruction going on behind it.

Jordi looked out. Ocean Avenue was a chaotic sea of rubble. People in all states of disfigurement were unsuccessfully attempting to escape. The other cars and trucks were crushed and twisted out of shape. Their occupants screamed to no avail. But Jordi's bus joggled along unmolested and unruffled. The children in it, especially Jordi, remained warm and safe.

Jordi snuggled even deeper into his seat and smiled happily.

◍

The classroom was light and bright.

He watched the drops of rain zigzag down the glass

panes. They gathered in the corner of the window, and then the crucial drop splattered the pool in all directions. The water running down the glass fascinated him. He looked through the clear streaks left by the rain drops, and then the thought screamed out —rain forest, rain trees! He could see them too—trees raining down—getting closer to the windows. He remembered stomping the garbage can—and then the feeling welled up in him. He smashed the glass with his fists.

Within seconds he broke the three windows in the room. He was striking out, fighting the trees now. He felt so good that he didn't notice the blood gushing from his hands. He screamed in triumph. The trees were receding—and then they were no more.

Sally just caught him as he passed out.

As he came out of the haze, he heard the doctor reassuring Sally. "There were a lot of nasty cuts—but no cut tendons, nerves, or anything important. Quite a lot of blood lost, but he'll be O.K. Keep the bandages on, and we'll remove the sutures in about a week."

⊙⊙

He went to school each morning and returned in the late afternoon. This went on week after week, month after month. He was not aware of the passage of time. Nor was he aware of the change taking place in him. It wasn't a big change, and yet in a way it was. Because he was becoming more comfortable. There were fewer terrors, fewer voices, less hiding in himself. There was so much going on outside of him—so much going on between him and the world, the world and its objects—the world that used to be an emptiness, a nothingness, a hole full of potential disaster. But only he knew of this new world-relating, and even he didn't "know" it. But he felt it—yes, he felt it. And yet it hardly showed. For, after all, as the months went by, there they were, as before—Sally and Jordi, Jordi and Sally—with only a few words between them now and then. But the words were increasing, and they were becoming more and more important as steppingstones between two people.

He called the week end the "different days." One Sunday when the streets, lacking their normal week day hustle and bustle, seemed empty, he had a thought, desert, desert—the big Sahara desert he had seen in the book. Then he thought, desert days, desert days.

But then Monday would roll around, and "Sally days" would be there again—and he would feel full and be somebody.

And so the time passed.

⊕

"Yi, yi! Yi, yi! I'll break them all, all, all. I'll break them all."

He put his heavy mittened fist through one after another of the windows.

"Jordi," she yelled. "Jordi! Stop, stop!"

She caught him and pinned his arms tightly against his body.

"What happened? Why did you break them? Don't you know, Jordi? Why?"

"I'm not Jordi. Leave me alone—I'm not Jordi. I'm me, but me isn't Jordi—not, not today, not today."

"I'm Sally today."

"Yes, you're still Sally—but me, I'm not Jordi, not today, not now."

"What's making you so angry?"

"This place is like an ice house, like an ice house today. I'm keeping my coat on. I won't take it off."

"Keep it on if you like, but that coat is Jordi's coat, and you said you're not Jordi, so why wear his coat?"

He ran over to the rack, tore his coat off, and jumped up and down on it.

"This is my coat, this one," he said, snatching the blue tweed overcoat off the hook.

"That isn't your coat. That belongs to Robert."

"It is Robert's coat, and today it is mine."

"How come it's yours today, Jordi?"

He didn't answer.

"Will it be yours tomorrow?"

"I don't know, I don't know. If I'm Jordi tomorrow, then it won't, but I don't know."

"Oh, I see. Then you must be Robert today."

"Yes, I'm him—I mean I'm me—but me is Robert."

"How come you are Robert?"

"I don't know. I just am Robert, that's all."

"How did you become him?"

He didn't answer.

"All right, Robert," she said. "When did you become him?"

He still ignored her.

"I thought you were Jordi when you left here yesterday."

"I was," he said. "I was—but he took Jordi away from me. He took him away."

"He?"

"Yes, he, Robert."

"Well, how did he, Robert, do that?"

"On my bus, on my school bus, that's how."

"On the bus?"

"He took my seat, he took it from me. He made me sit in his. I had to sit in his. I said, 'Give me my seat, give me my Jordi seat,' but they laughed."

"Who, Jordi?"

He ignored her.

"I mean who laughed?"

He still didn't answer.

"I mean who laughed, Robert?"

"Now I understand you, now I do. It was the train man. The train man, he laughed at me and said, "Take Robert's seat. All the seats are the same. We can't waste time. Come on, kid, take Robert's seat!"

"Well, where is Jordi now?" she asked.

"Over there," he said, pointing to Robert. "Over there, that's the Jordi boy, the one that sat in the Jordi seat."

Sally walked over to the coat rack and took down John's big brown coat. It was much too large for her. It came down to her ankles, and the sleeves flapped below her hands.

"I guess I've got the wrong coat on," she said, flapping the sleeves up and down.

"Yes, Sally, that coat isn't yours. That's John's coat—Lisa's teacher, John."

"Then who am I? If I'm wearing John's coat, who am I?"

"Oh, come on, you're silly."

"I'm silly. I guess I am silly with this great big coat on."

"I mean Sally—Sally silly, silly Sally."

"Yes, Jordi, I'm Sally. Maybe silly, but still Sally, and, no matter whose coat I put on, I am still Sally."

She went back to the rack and put one coat on after

another. Each time she put another coat on, she asked, "Who am I?" And each time he repeated, "You're Sally, I know you're Sally."

Then she took his hand and said, "Let's go up to William's office." When she got to the director's office, she asked him if he could leave for a few minutes. He said, "Hi, Jordi," as he closed the door behind him. Then Sally sat down in William's chair.

"Whose chair is this?"

"William's chair."

"Where is William?"

"William just went out."

"So who am I?"

"You, you're Sally—silly Silly," he grinned.

She got up. "Sit here, in William's chair." He sat down.

"Where is William?" she asked.

"Oh, he's still outside, Sally. You know that."

"Well, where are you sitting?"

"I'm sitting in the big chair."

"Whose chair?"

"The William chair."

"And who are you?"

He looked into her eyes very solemnly. Then his face crinkled into a big grin, and he said, "I'm Jordi. Yes, Sally, I'm truly Jordi."

∞

"You know, Sally—the trees are gone."

"What trees, Jordi?"

"The rain trees."

"Oh? Tell me about them."

"The trees that rain down—the trees from the rain forest. You saw them yesterday when I beat them off. The day I got my hands sewed up."

"That wasn't yesterday. That was a year ago, Jordi—a year ago. Remember the calendar we studied, Jordi? Remember the days, the weeks, the months—years?"

"I remember. Yes, I do, Sally."

"Yesterday is just a day ago—the day before today, the day before you got up this morning. You hurt your hands many days ago—a year ago."

"Yes, Sally, I understand. It wasn't yesterday; it was twelve months ago.

"But, Sally, let's talk. I know about days, but the trees—I want to talk about them."

"I'm sorry, Jordi. Go ahead, tell me about the trees."

"Well, the trees—when it rains now, just rain drops come down, not like before Sally."

"Before?"

"You remember rain forest, rain trees—coming down to look for me. They were so scary, so scary," he said, trembling.

"You must have been angry, Jordi. You must have been scared of being angry."

"Angry, me angry. But the trees looked angry."

"Jordi, do you know what a rain forest is? Come, let's look it up in the encyclopedia."

She read the big book out loud. She read all about equatorial rain forests and rain trees and explained the material to him in detail. She ended by saying, "So, you see, Jordi, rain forest doesn't mean trees or forests raining down."

Jordi was fascinated. "Sally, does it say all that in the book?"

"Yes, Jordi, it's all here in this encyclopedia."

"Encyclopedia." He repeated the word several times.

"Would you like to be able to read this book, Jordi?"

"Could I, Sally?"

"Well, you can learn to read, Jordi, if you like."

"Could I, Sally, could I?"

"Yes, Jordi."

∞

"Toosies, toosies—hop, skip, and jump." Then she lost interest and walked over to him.

"Hi, kid, wanna play?"

He said, "Play, play, go away."

"Hey, you're funny, sonny."

She took his hand and pulled him along. But he yanked his hand away.

He thought, she will leave me.

He ran to the corner and stood perfectly still. Maybe now she wouldn't notice him, but she ran after him and once again took his hand.

"C'mon, kid, let's play. . . . What's your name? Me, I'm Muriel. Who are you? What does your mommy call you?"

"Jordi."

"Georgie, porgie, puddin' and pie, kiss the girls and made them cry."

"Kiss, piss, fiss. Georgie, porgie."

He screwed up his face. "Georgie, Georgie—who is Georgie?"

"You silly dilly—you—you're Georgie. . . . Dilly,

dilly—Willie, Willie? You're funny, honey. Honey, bunny—money—yummy.

"Let's play, Georgie—let's play. Muriel will show you. You're yummy—yum yum, Georgie."

"Jordi," he screamed. "Jordi—I'm Jordi. Tell—Sally, tell—me, I'm Jordi."

"Oh, Jordi. Lordy Jordi—no more porgie Georgie.

"Well, I'm Lisa—Lisa, not Muriel. Like the cigar Daddy smokes—Muriel.

"What's that you're jiggling, Jordi?"

"Jiggling?" He laughed. "I'm jiggling my jiggler. Jiggle, jiggle—wiggle, wiggle—my friend, my friend—my jiggler."

"Make me a jiggler, Jordi—would you, huh?"

"Sally? Where are you, Sally?"

"Here, Jordi, right here. Come, Jordi, Lisa, let's go to lunch."

◯◯

"Promise, Sally, promise we'll take a train ride all over the old stations. I'll show them all to you, Sally—the IRT, the BMT. Will you come with me, Sally—will you?"

"Of course, Jordi. It sounds so nice."

"When, Sally, when?"

"Now, if you like—yes, right now."

"Will we pass the water tower on the way to the station?"

"Yes, we will go down by way of the tower. But first finish lunch, Jordi."

"Why, Sally?"

"Aren't you hungry, Jordi?"

"No."

"But if you eat, you'll grow big and strong."

Jordi dashed from the table, ran upstairs, and grabbed the yardstick. He broke half a dozen windows before Sally caught up with him.

"Why, Jordi? Why?"

He didn't answer.

Sally held him closer. He yanked himself out of her arms and ran out of the room. Sally followed.

She sat with him the entire afternoon. Not a word passed between them that day, the next, and the next —not for three weeks. They just walked around together. Jordi knew she was there, but his feeling of emptiness just cut him off from her and everything else.

Then he felt like taking a train ride, and he thought of Sally, and he forgot to be silent.

"Sally, can we take the train today?"

"Yes. We can, and we shall."

After lunch they walked about eight blocks to the water tower.

"It's a lovely tower, Sally."

"How is it lovely, Jordi?"

"It's high and it's quiet and it's alone."

"You like it, Jordi?"

"I like it."

"How much, a little or a lot?" Sally asked, demonstrating with her hands.

"Much, much—this much and more, Sally—much more. A lot—a big lot."

"I guess you love the tower, Jordi."

He felt the good bursting feeling well up in his chest.

"I love the tower. I do love the water tower."

"Wonderful, Jordi, wonderful. Now you know what love feels like."

"Love. I feel love—I feel love, Sally?"

His face glowed, the feeling spread through him, and he felt warm and nice and comfortable. And then the feeling evaporated and in its place left a scare. He took Sally's hand and said, "Let's take the train now."

On the train he drew his eyes away from the tunnel and his ever-arriving, wonderful stations. He faced her.

"Sally, yesterday I didn't like you, not even a little much."

"You mean you disliked me, Jordi?"

"I did, I did dislike you."

"How did I hurt you yesterday, Jordi?"

"Sally, I want to be little. I want to be a boy." Then the words exploded forth: "You said I'd be big and strong."

"Oh," she said, "three weeks ago, yesterday."

"Yes, Sally. If I'm big, I won't be a boy any more. I don't want to be big, Sally—just a boy, just Jordi."

"You must have been very angry with me."

"Yes, Sally, yes. Let me be little—let me be me, just Jordi."

"Jordi, you will always be you—and some day you will understand this better."

"I like you now, Sally."

"I like you too, Jordi. But if you don't like me—if sometimes you dislike me or dislike me much, hate me—that's all right too."

But he had lost interest and was watching the stations again.

∞

The monkey bars, crisscrossing up and down, forward and backward, intrigued him. There was no question that his jiggler pointed in their direction. But what if he got caught in the middle of all that iron? What if he couldn't get out?

He walked over cautiously and touched the closest bar. It was cold. A sinister chill ran through him. But the jiggler pointed in that direction again. This time he touched a bar warmed by the sun. This felt different, more inviting, but he was still afraid. It looked like a wonderful toy to climb over and swing from. And it looked like an awful monster that could tangle you up, crush you, and kill you.

He couldn't move from the spot. He wanted to run toward and away from it at the same time. Indecision paralyzed him. His face was flushed, and he ground his teeth. Tears streamed down his cheeks, but his legs remained planted.

Her low voice, soft and smooth, said, "Try it. It's fun, Jordi—fun—a toy. I'll show you."

She swung from a high bar, bringing her legs out perpendicular to her body. Then from the top of them she yelled, "Yo-ho, Jordi! It's nice up here."

His legs kicked out of their invisible trap. "Wait for me, Sally. I'm coming to look at the sky too."

On the way back to school he said, "I was afraid it would tangle me."

"Oh?"

"The cold ones. The warm ones were nicer."

Sally told him how the sun warmed some of the bars. She then told him that he could tangle himself but could not get tangled by it—or by anything else that wasn't alive.

Before he went to sleep that night he thought about it a lot and he began to get the feeling of the difference between living and nonliving objects. By the next day some of the magic of the monkey bars was gone—but so was the monster.

They went back the next day. He looked at them but suddenly realized how thin the bars were. Maybe they couldn't hold him. What if he fell through them? They were so shiny. He could feel the whole structure crashing down on him.

"Let's go back, Sally."

"Why?"

"I'm afraid. Please, Sally—please."

"Let's play on the bars for a while first."

"No."

"They can't hurt you, Jordi."

"But if they fall, Sally."

"They are made of iron—very strong stuff, Jordi. They can hold twenty of us."

"But not me, Sally—not me."

"Oh, Jordi, so you're not afraid of the bars being weak?"

"I am afraid."

"You're afraid that you won't hold yourself up, Jordi. But you're strong. Look at your arms and legs—how sturdy they are."

"I'm strong like the iron, Sally?"

"Well, not like the iron—but good and strong. Strong enough, Jordi, so that you can hold yourself on the bars. That is, if you don't want to fall, Jordi."

"No, no, I don't want to fall."

"Then you won't fall, Jordi. Let's go."

They played on the bars, and it was fun. He felt strong swinging up and back. He smiled at her as they looked at the blue sky.

"Fun, Jordi?"

"Yes—and I'm strong, Sally. Me—Jordi—I'm strong."

He even forgot to take his jiggler out on the way home from school.

⊙⊙

Several months later he sat at his mother's sewing table.

He looked at the crayons and took out all the short pieces. That left him seven long ones. He couldn't make up his mind. First he started with orange, then red, then black. He finally started to fill the fish in with purple.

But the point was worn down. He tried awfully hard but couldn't stay within the lines. He held his hand stiff and tried not to bend his wrist, but this only made it worse. Tears streamed down his cheeks, and he could hardly see. He held his right hand with his left, but to no avail. Grief and hopelessness flooded him. He heard himself thinking, can't, can't, can't— Jordi can't. Jordi can't. No good, no good, no good.

There was little of the fish left now. The purple made wilder and wilder streaks all over the paper. This time there was no hesitancy in his choice. He took the red crayon. Holding it like a knife, he stabbed the paper again and again. Then he took the black and blotted out the remains of the fish altogether. He took the sharp pencil and stabbed and tore and stabbed and tore over and over again.

The paper was in shreds now. His sobbing tore out of him in spasms. It was interrupted only by short gasps of breath. His body twisted to and fro, and his shoulders heaved up and down. He felt himself drowning in anguish.

Through his tears he suddenly saw the tattered paper. It was monstrous. This torn-up red, purple, black, stabbed, blotted-out fish was horror itself. He screamed and ran. He could feel the thing chasing him. This bleeding, stumpy thing he had wounded. This monster he had manufactured.

The form and color of it kaleidoscoped. He pictured it short, round, fat, tall, black, purple, sharp, dull with jagged holes and hating him. He stopped. He hit his jaw with his closed fist. He hit himself again and again.

His face was very swollen, but the monster had gone. Only a piece of colored paper remained. He crumpled it into a ball and dropped it into the basket.

He heard the key in the door, and then she came in. He heard her say, "Oh, God, oh God. My God. Why, why? Your face, your face, my baby, my baby. Why, why did you do it, why?"

He let himself be led into the bathroom, and the cold compress felt good. He heard her sobbing but couldn't understand why.

"But, Mama, I feel good. I do, I do feel good."

"Why did you beat yourself? Why, Jordi, why?"

"It was the fish monster. I had to get it away—I just had to. It was—oh, Mama, I don't want to hit myself. I don't want to. I don't know, I don't know—how—how. Oh, Mama, help me," he cried, and then she stopped crying.

He felt himself held by her and felt his bruised cheek being kissed. He snuggled into her arms. Then she led him into the living room and gave him the chocolate bar she had in her bag. He stopped crying, ate it, and felt better.

"I like you. Mom, I like you."

"I love you, Jordi. I love you very much."

"How much, Mom? How much?"

"A great big bunch and then some—more than anything, more than anything in this whole world."

"Gee, I feel nice, Mom. It feels good in here." He pointed to his chest. "It feels warm and good in here."

"I'm glad. I'm so glad, Jordi."

He went outside and walked to the water tower. He sat and stared at it for a while. Then he walked around it and looked at it some more. After a while he started to walk home. He made sure his jiggler was in his pocket but didn't take it out. Just knowing he had it with him made him feel safer.

On the way home he thought about Sally and wondered what words they would rhyme in school. Then he thought of the word "rhyme," and then "slime" and "climb." He pictured himself climbing the water tower. On top of it he would be away and higher than anyone else. But he would have to come down to see Sally and her and him too. Then he thought, her and him, Mama and Papa.

When they ate supper, his jaw ached, and he thought about it.

"Do you feel all right?" his father asked.

"Yes, yes."

"But your jaw, Jordi, does it hurt?"

"My jaw—yes, it hurts. It does hurt."

"I'm sorry it hurts, Jordi."

"Me, I'm sorry too. I'm sorry my jaw hurts."

He rubbed it a little too hard and winced.

After supper he was very tired. He lay on his bed thinking about things for a while. In a very short time he fell asleep.

He dreamed that he was walking on the kitchen floor. He walked up and back, swinging his jiggler to and fro. Suddenly he realized that the floor had a big fish outlined on it, and nearby lay a great big purple crayon. He took the crayon and started to color the fish. But then the crayon turned into a Pogo stick. Jordi rode the Pogo—jumping from spot to spot and depositing purple wherever he landed. Soon the whole fish was purple—and there wasn't a spot outside of the lines.

Then a funny thing happened. The fish rose up from the floor and became a real live purple fish. Then it said, "I like you Jordi. You made me a nice color, and I'll always be your friend."

Then he tied a long string all around the fish and led him through the deserted street like a dog on a leash. And people woke up and began to fill the streets. He wasn't afraid, though, because he had his fish friend with him, who was bigger even than a big dog.

He got up the next morning feeling that there was more to him. He felt as though there was more of him than his usual self—sort of like a piece had been added. He looked in the dresser mirror and felt disappointed that there was no addition to himself. His dimensions were all the same. He was no heavier and no taller.

But the feeling stuck with him. There was just more of him, even if he couldn't see it. Maybe there was more inside him—inside, where he couldn't see but sometimes felt different things.

The feeling made him walk differently. His feet moved more importantly; his steps were surer. Everything about himself felt more solid. When he got on the bus that morning, he almost felt it creak down in response to his added something. He remembered nothing of his dream. It was as if it never happened.

When he got to school, he and Sally rhymed words for a while and then sat down at the long low table.

"I feel funny, Sally."

"Oh?"

"Sort of like more."

"Like more, Jordi?"

"More—draw, draw. Let's draw, Sally."

She took down a big box of crayons and paper.

For a while he just drew lines—then broader lines, and then boxes and circles here and there. Then he drew a series of dots from one corner of the page to the other. Then he drew lines connecting the dots.

"Sally, could we fill in something?"

"Sure. What would you like to fill in, Jordi?"

He didn't answer.

"Here. Here is a triangle, Jordi."

"A triangle?" he asked.

"Yes." She explained how a triangle consisted of three sides and three angles—one between each pair of sides. Then she drew a circle and a rectangle and defined and explained each of them to him.

Jordi was intrigued with what he heard. Listening to her was great fun.

"Gee, I like this, Sally. I like to play this way."

"Me too," she said.

Then he took a purple crayon and started to fill in the large triangle—the one he now knew was an equilateral triangle. He was very careful, but, unwittingly, he moved just outside the lower left angle.

"Oh, oh," he moaned, "Sally, I feel funny. Oh."

"What's wrong, Jordi? What? Tell me."

He hit himself with his closed fist again and again.

"Hold my hand, Sally. Help me—hold me."

She held his hands between hers as he moaned, "Oh, oh." Then she managed to get him on her lap. She bent over him, held her arms around him, and hugged him tightly.

He felt warm and safe.

After a while he stopped moaning. But she continued to hold him. Soon she started to hum and sing to him—and after a few minutes he hummed along with her. They sat humming and singing for more than an hour. Then they walked around the room and looked at all the new pictures recently placed on the walls.

They had meat loaf, potatoes, and green peas for lunch. Jordi attacked it with relish and even ate some more potatoes before he gulped down his Jell-O.

When they were back upstairs—sitting at the table—Sally started to talk.

"Why were you angry at yourself, Jordi?"

"Angry?"

"Yes—before lunch when you hit yourself and asked me to hold your hands?"

"Oh—I was angry?" he asked with some wonderment. Then he answered himself. "Yes, I was. I went outside the line." Tears started to fill his eyes. "I went outside the line. I couldn't help it—I just couldn't."

"The line, Jordi?"

"Yes, when I filled in with the crayon."

"I see."

"Do you, Sally?"

"Yes. I understand. But, Jordi, you don't have to draw perfectly. It's all right to go outside the line. I'll love you anyway.

"Jordi, you draw just for fun. If it has to be perfect, it's no fun."

"Perfect?" he questioned.

"Yes—you know—just so, all within the line—exactly so. Nothing—nothing is perfect."

"But, Sally, if it's outside the line the triangle won't be a triangle anymore. It will be all over. It will be like wild—like a panther."

"But, Jordi, even if it isn't a triangle anymore, it's OK. And a little bit won't matter anyway. It will still be a triangle. And anyway, Jordi, a drawing isn't a living thing. But, regardless of how you draw, Jordi, you will still be you, and I'll love you inside or outside the line."

"A drawing isn't a living thing," he repeated. "A drawing isn't a living thing.

"Draw an empty fish—draw a fish, Sally."

She outlined a big fish on a large white sheet of paper.

He filled it in with purple. Then he looked at her—and scribbled the crayon outside the outline. He looked at her again. And they both started to laugh together. And they laughed and laughed until their bellies hurt. Then she hugged him and hugged him and kissed his cheek. And it didn't feel bruised at all.

After several months Jordi had learned a considerable amount about addition, subtraction, and the multiplication tables and some facts about division.

One day he asked if they could talk more about the angles—triangles and rectangles. Sally told him all about degrees in angles. Then she went on and explained about circles and area and volume. Jordi was very attentive and absorbed it readily. But then Sally explained that this would be discussed later on in high school and college. She described high school and college and working. Jordi listened but wasn't too interested. Later on they resumed their reading work, and he liked the way she looked when he read a whole page from the reader without stopping.

Just before he went home that day he turned to her and said, "Sally, you really became a teacher in this room."

⊙⊙

He got off the bus.

"Hello, Sally."

"Hi, Jordi."

50

"School is nice. I like it. The public, it's the public I don't like."

"The public?"

"Yes, they—the strangers. I was with strangers the whole Saturday and Sunday—the whole week end."

"But you were home, Jordi."

"Home, home with the public—with strangers."

"Your mother and father were home, Jordi."

"They were public also—they were all strangers. They were all away from me—not close like you and me now here in school, Sally."

"All? Who else was there?"

"The funny baby and Tillie and Joseph."

"Funny baby?"

"Billy—Cousin Billy. He's a little bitty baby."

"But you said he was funny, Jordi."

"Well—he was crying—they couldn't make him stop. They all jumped around the room—and Billy made such funny faces. I laughed. They made mean faces at me. I laughed some more—his face was so funny. They tried to make me stop. Then one of the public —she hit me."

"She? Your mother?"

"Yes—but this week end she was no mother. She was a stranger."

"You mean because she didn't understand you—she was strange."

"Yes—but you understand me, Sally."

"Not always. Sometimes it takes time. And sometimes it takes the people at home time."

"Like sometimes I can't understand them?"

"That's right, Jordi."

"Let's rhyme words, Sally."

"OK."

They sat down at the table.

"Cat," she began.
"Bat."
"Fat."
"Sat."
It was soon time for lunch.

∞

He looked at the ceiling and thought of the sky, the earth, the street, and the subway station. He remembered somebody saying that the world was round. He pictured a round globe hanging in mid-air and then thought of everybody walking to and fro on the big ball. Then he pictured a staircase going down into the ball and coming to a bright station. He saw a train run through the globe and stop at the station. A sandy-haired little boy got on the train holding a string attached to a doorknob between his right thumb and forefinger. The train left the station and rode all around the inside of the globe. The boy walked from one car to the next and finally came to the first one. He hung the doorknob out the front window.

Then the train followed the jiggler—zig, zag, this way and that. Yes, he was using the magic string knob to lead the train all over the inside of the earth. It was actually working. The magic jiggler was controlling the train.

Then he realized that the boy was getting larger. He had the same face and the same sandy hair, but he was big now—very big. Soon he was a giant and almost filled the whole car. He could tell that the boy giant was afraid of nothing. There he was with his jiggler and his train going wherever he liked. Nobody could stop him. The earth was his.

Then Jordi saw the boy wave the jiggler around outside the front window. And the train left the track, and there was no track in front of it or anywhere in sight. But the train went faster than ever—whiz, whiz, whiz. It cut through the earth. It was cutting the globe up like a big piece of cake, only it was doing it from the inside. And then he saw big pieces of the globe caving in all over the train. But the giant boy and his jiggler led the train right through it all to slice up the earth some more—and more and more.

When he looked at the top of the earth, people were running all over the place, but they couldn't get away. They were being buried by the big cave-ins. Buildings were crumbling all over. It was dark, but the sky was bright blood red. And in the light of the redness Jordi could see the earth and many things on it falling down, down and crumbling all up. The giant had a big smile on his face now.

The earth, and everything on it, was gone. Only the train remained, and the giant boy and his jiggler led it from station to lighted station through space.

Jordi rolled over and fell asleep at once.

∞

The bath felt very nice. It was warm, and he was alone. He pushed the piece of wood around the tub and watched it skim over his knees and then back again over his belly. Then he held it down on the bottom of the tub and let it go suddenly, watching it shoot to the surface. He let the wood float and then dropped the bar of soap on it from different heights. Splash, splash, but the wood popped right up again. Then he thought of his penis. First he squeezed it; then he rubbed it up and down. It felt nice, and it was good to be alone. When his penis stood up, he stared at it a while and wondered how this magic took place. There it was again much bigger than before and standing straight up. He thought, first it's like the jiggler, then it's like the water tower.

After a while he got up and soaped himself all over. Then sat down and let the water get real cloudy and soapy.

He lay on his back, and almost his whole body was hidden by the cloudy water. He pushed his foot through. He could see it but not the rest of his leg. He suddenly felt that his foot was detached from his leg and the rest of his body. He became very frightened and lifted his foot quickly, and there it was, still part of the rest of him. He felt much better but didn't dare lift his foot that way again—at least not in the cloudy water.

He played with the wooden boat some more. It glided over his belly. Then he let the dirty water out of the tub and let in new clean clear water.

Then he felt interested in his belly button. He looked at it and screwed his finger around in it. Then he noticed how a little water remained in his belly button each time he brought his belly up out of the water.

He had a funny thought: Button is to close up something. Belly button closes up the belly. What if it opened up and a little water got in?

He could already see himself swelling, swelling, swelling and then—pop—exploding.

And yet he knew with his thoughts, that it wouldn't happen. He knew that his belly button wouldn't open, and he even doubted that it had anything to do with his insides anyway. But the feeling about it and the picture of water leaking in persisted. So he felt a little silly but got up and dried himself. He made sure no water remained in his belly button.

⚭

He sat with them and stared at his father. He waited for him to talk. He liked to hear his voice. It was soft and deep and made him feel warm. The thunder was the same way too. His mother's voice was high and thinner. Sometimes it stuck and cut, but sometimes it was high and bright like lightning.

"Jordi, would you like to go to the zoo?"

"Yes."

And then they left the house. He held his hand and let himself be led even though he knew the train route they were taking.

When they got off at the station, they had a long block to walk to the zoo. He kicked a can he found all along the way. Then they saw the elephants, monkeys, and lions.

His father knew that the panthers pleased him most, so they stayed at the cage for a long time.

Jordi watched the animal pace up and down and wondered what would happen if it got loose. He liked its shininess and the rippling way it moved. Woosh, woosh—he could see it tear through the crowd and everybody running in all directions. Everybody but me, he thought as he took his jiggler out and dangled it.

His father bought some popcorn and peanuts. They sat on the bench and fed themselves and the squirrels. The squirrels pleased him very much, taking the nuts from his fingers the way they did.

∞

"Boy, is he angry! Jesus Christ, he is *mad!* Boy! Look at him—just look, Sally."

He had the magazine open to an insurance ad. There was a picture of a train wreck and a man looking at it with a startled, worried expression on his face.

"Wow! This man is *angry*. Wow, is he angry—an angry man, a truly angry man."

Jordi walked up and down the room. He was too excited to do anything else that day. He felt this man's feeling. And seeing a man whose feeling was his feeling in a big magazine was very exciting. He was so excited he hardly ate lunch that day. He carried the magazine with him wherever he went for a whole week. Then he asked Sally if they could hang the magazine on the bulletin board. They tried tacking it up but finally settled on just putting up the page with the picture.

He walked up to the wall again and again. Then, almost a month after they put the picture up, he left Sally at the low table and walked over to Lisa and John. He stood close to them and watched Lisa make the Indian bead ring.

"Hi, kid—hi," she said.

"Hello, hello. Come with me, Lisa. I want to show you."

She looked to John.

"Go, Lisa," he said. "Go with Jordi."

"All right, Jordi Pordi. Let's amble, let's scramble, and let's go—but slow—ho, ho."

He led her to the picture on the wall. He pointed to it. "Jesus Christ, is he angry! Boy, he is! He is—he is sure truly angry."

"Jordi, Pordi, let's play jacks. OK? Jacks, facts—let's go, Jo."

"But, Lisa, the man—look, look at him—how he looks. Boy, is he mad! He is *sore!*"

"Sore, tore—what for?" She ran back to John.

He looked at the picture again, shrugged his shoulders, and went back to Sally at the table.

"That Lisa—Muriel kid is funny. Angry—angry—she doesn't know what it is—angry. Funny, honey—that girl is funny. She sure is."

"Well, we're not all the same, Jordi."

"But angry—Sally, I told her about angry—and she walked away."

"About anger, Jordi," she corrected.

"Yes, Sally—about anger."

He went on. "She is funny, that kid. She is funny."

"Well, we all have problems, Jordi."

"Problems. Gee, that's a funny way to say it—problems. What do you mean—problems?"

"Well, like you, Jordi—when you were afraid of the monkey bars."

"Yes, Sally—and like the garbage cans and the rain trees."

"That's right, Jordi."

"But, Sally, that was the old Jordi.

"Do you remember, do you remember the old Jordi, Sally? Do you remember him? He couldn't ride a bike.

He was afraid of the cans. Sometimes he was afraid to talk. He had problems. He had lots of problems, Sally —boy, oh boy, he truly had problems.

"But now, Sally, now the new Jordi is here. He can walk and ride and talk and go on the monkey bars. He can get angry and he can say 'gee whizz,' and he can draw outside the line.

"And, Sally, the new Jordi—me—I know about triangles and I can read too."

"You sure can, Jordi—and how you can."

Lisa walked by. She was talking to herself.

"Muriel is my name—and it's the same, the same."

Jordi looked at Sally and then asked, "Is her problem showing, Sally? Is Lisa's problem showing?"

"Yes, I guess it is, Jordi. You could say that. Her problem is showing."

"Sally, it's a long time, a long time. Isn't it, Sally?"

"A long time what is? What, Jordi? What is a long time?"

"You, Sally. You—you and me. Is it years? Is it years and years, Sally?"

"Jordi, it's years—but it seems longer to me too."

"Sally, it's like you were always. Like when I think of it—it's like it was black before."

"Black, Jordi?"

"Last night I thought of before. It seemed so long ago, like it wasn't. Then I knew it was—and when I thought of it—I saw it like a darkness. It was all black —I got scared. I jumped out of bed—and put the light on. Then I felt better. Then I thought, Sally, and the blackness became gone. I said 'Sally,' then I turned off the light—and it was dark—but it was light."

different qualities of the same article and about the differences these made in relative money value. He listened attentively and then said, "Gee, Sally, you know a lot of a lot of a lot of things."

Then Sally stopped walking and turned him around to face her. She held his shoulders and looked into his eyes and said, "Jordi, today you talked to a stranger. You just walked into that store and talked to somebody you didn't know. Not only that, you asked for something and nothing bad happened, Jordi. It came out fine."

"I talked to a stranger," he repeated. "I talked to a stranger—you know, Sally—and then she wasn't so strange anymore."

Then they walked back to school to practice stoop ball.

It wasn't at all easy. Sally told him to be careful of cars when he went to retrieve the ball. And he did a lot of retrieving. Each time he hit a point the ball went over his head. But he learned fast, and before long he was a stoopball player.

After an hour his arm hurt, but he kept playing. After a while he tallied up points, and then it was even more fun. But when his arm felt real heavy, he said, "Let's rhyme words or something, Sally."

He played lots of stoop ball after that, both at school and at home. He carried the ball constantly, and on some days he was so busy holding and squeezing it that he hardly remembered his jiggler.

∞

"I can climb the bars now, Sally."
"What was that, Jordi? I didn't hear you."

"The bars, monkey bars—now I can climb on them and play."

"Yes, you sure can."

"Sally, it's the bars and things, other things too."

"Yes, there's been much, Jordi—many things."

And there were things, many things. There was incident after incident. There were bars, many bars—bars to cross, bars to climb, bars to knock down—and they did it. And it was hard work. But they struggled, and the bars came down.

OO

Spring had come. It was a warm day.

"How about going over to the playground, Jordi?"

"What will we do there, Sally?"

"Well, there's the monkey bars."

"No, no, Sally, let's do something else."

"Why? Are you afraid of something, Jordi?"

"No, no," he hastened to reassure her.

"It's just—well." He seemed embarrassed.

"Jordi, come on now, what's doing?" she asked.

"Well, Sally—well, the other children playing there—well, Sally—well—they're small, Sally. They're so small."

"You're right, Jordi. I hadn't realized—you are bigger than the other children. I guess I sometimes forget you're a big boy now. You're over twelve now—over twelve years old."

She seemed very pleased with it all. He couldn't understand why but kind of felt happy because she seemed to feel so good.

After lunch Sally said she wanted to read something important and would he like to busy himself for a while. He welcomed being alone and told her he would be on the stoop of the school building.

He sat there a while, and then he took out his jiggler. He noticed how hard it was to get it out of his pocket. Then he took the ball from his other pocket. He weighed and balanced them, one in each hand. Then he thought to himself, my old jiggler. He put it back in his pocket and began to play stoop ball. Then for the first time in his memory the jiggler bothered him. He felt the shaft of the doorknob dig into his thigh each time he threw the ball. He took the jiggler out again and went into the building to find Sally at her desk.

"Will you hold my jiggler for me, Sally? I want to play stoop ball."

She said, "Sure, Jordi. Here, I'll put it in my desk drawer."

He went outside and resumed his solitary game of stoop ball.

⊙⊙

Several weeks later it was a beautiful, dry frosty day. They went to the playground, and Jordi walked around for a while, just breathing in the crispy air and feeling good.

He watched the children on the monkey bars and thought that they looked just like the little monkeys in the zoo.

Sally sat on the bench and read while he explored the entire playground. Then he saw the group of boys playing handball. They were about ten years old. There were three of them, and the very dark boy yelled out to him.

"Hey, fella, how about some handball? I need a partner."

Jordi said, "I don't know how."

"Don't worry, I'll show you. My name is Billy. What's your name?"

"I'm Jordi."

"Come on, Jordi." Billy beckoned, and Jordi joined the group.

∞

He had no idea that four years had passed since he first entered the "ice house."

When Sally told him about the impending examination, he vaguely remembered the ink blots, the cold stethoscope, and somebody talking and bothering him.

After they talked about it a while he lost interest, and they went back to what they were doing.

∞

This twelve-year-old, white, sandy-haired boy has been examined, tested, and interviewed by the psychological and psychiatric diagnostic and planning staff.

His size, weight, and appearance are not unusual. There is no evidence of physical impairment of any kind. There is no evidence of organicity. Contact is good, and attention span is fair. He hesitates at the beginning of the interview situation but soon adjusts and relates adequately.

He is well oriented in all spheres and demonstrates good memory function for both recent and past events. There is at present no evidence of secondary phenomena, hallucinations and delusions not being demonstrable. Impulse control is fair. His affective display is somewhat shallower than normal but is appropriate for the most part.

TAT and Rorschach as well as pressure during interviewing indicate and elicit considerable underlying hostility and anxiety. There is also evidence of an inappropriate naivete and a rather infantile approach to himself and his place in the world. There is a paucity of general information mainly pertaining to history, geography, sports events, etc. There is, however, indication of a superior I.Q.—a surprisingly good vocabulary and intermittent areas of erudition well beyond the level of a twelve-year-old. There is also evidence of originality and perhaps even of artistry.

Jordi is fearful of contact with his contemporaries, and this can be understood on many levels, among them his great inexperience in this area.

There is evidence of increasing obsessive defensive maneuvers. This is, however, felt to be a good prognostic sign, since the latter is probably a substitute for his earlier autistic existence.

Diagnosis: At this time deferred.

Prognosis: In view of excellent progress, the future looks relatively bright—we hope.

Recommendations: Discharge from this institution within a year. Jordi should then be ready for formal psychoanalytical treatment while attending an ordinary school. We feel that the latter school must be small and provide for individual understanding and attention.

At the time of discharge we will refer Jordi to one of our list of child psychoanalysts, who may then have a conference with our staff and Jordi's teacher.

The Beginning

⚭

"Jordi, how do you feel about going to another school?"

"Another school?" he asked, obviously confused. "Will you be there? Will you be there with me, Sally?"

She went on. "Jordi, you don't understand. Do you remember we once talked about more grown-up schools, about high schools and colleges?"

"Yes, I remember, but will you be there, Sally?"

"No, Jordi, I won't be there—but you will learn a great deal more about angles, about history and many interesting things. And there will be other teachers there, and you will meet children your age there too."

"I don't want to go, Sally. I want to stay with you."

"You're not leaving yet, Jordi. It won't be for another six months."

"Do I have to go? Do I have to, Sally? Who will I talk to? Who will tell me I'm Jordi if I get lost—who, Sally?"

He began to cry, and she hugged him to her.

"You won't get lost, Jordi. You're lots better now. Your problem hardly shows anymore—that's why you don't have to stay. You can go to a regular school."

"You mean Lisa can't leave?" he said through his tears.

"No, she can't leave, Jordi. Besides, Jordi, you will have Dr. Mills to talk to. You will see him every day after school."

"Oh, Sally—oh, why did you tell me, why? Now my problems will show—now mine will show."

"Let them show, Jordi, and cry all you like. And, Jordi," she said, "you will visit me. You can come now and then, and I'll come and see you at home every few months. We can talk on the phone too."

"Everything hurts. Please, please, don't say any more, Sally."

But Sally said much more. They talked and talked about his departure from the school.

And then only two days remained before Jordi would leave. Four and a half years had passed since he entered the "ice house."

"Jordi, in two days you will go to your new school, but remember you can visit here."

He suddenly swirled about, faced her, and yelled, "You hate me, you hate me. You lied, you lied. You never liked me never. And I hate you, I hate you."

He picked up a blackboard eraser and threw it, shattering the nearest window.

Then he ran out of the room and out of the building. He just ran and ran, too dazed to think or watch where he was going. But he soon found himself on the subway and in the front car of the Lexington Avenue express.

He rode all over New York and cried most of the time. Then he thought about Sally and the times gone by. Then he thought about their talks of the last six months.

When he got back, it was six o'clock, but everybody was still there. Even his mother and father were there.

Then he saw her, and she said, "Jordi, I'm so glad to see you. I'm so glad to see you, Jordi."

He looked at her and said, "I came back, I came back. Sally, I came back to leave."

Lisa and David

To Nathan Freeman M. D.
Teacher and Friend

This is a love story of two exceptional children.

The place is a residential treatment center.

The time, one year after admission, is a crucial period in their lives during which communication becomes possible.

September 15, 1959–September 15, 1960

∞

"A big fat sow, a big black cow—and how and how and how.

"A big fat cow, a big black sow—and how and how and how.

"A cow, a cow; a sow, a sow—big and fat, big and fat; so they sat—so they sat, they sat; so they sat."

She hopped around the room, first on one foot, then on the other. On her left foot she always said, "sow," and on her right foot, "cow." She sat down on the floor each time she said, "They sat, they sat." But in seconds she was up again—hopping around the room and, in a loud, clear, high-pitched voice, saying, "A cow, a cow; a sow, a sow—black, black, black, black, black, black, black, black." Her voice changed. She was shrieking now. Then she sat down, held her head with her hands, and moved it up and back, moaning softly. "Dark, dark, dark, dark, dark—so, so, so, so dark."

⊙⊙

"Fuddy-dud-dud,   fuddy-dud-dud-duddy—fud-fud-duddy fud-fud.

"Scudy-rud—rud-scud, rud-scud; duddy-scud fud rud, duddy scud fud rud."

She sat in the corner and repeated the sequence over and over again. John tried to engage her in a sensible conversation—but to no avail. She listened to him, looked at him, and repeated the sequence again and again.

David listened and wondered what she meant. He finally gave up and thought about a big calendar clock he had seen a year ago.

That night before he fell asleep he had a fantasy. The sky was absolutely clear of clouds, the air cool, crisp, and dry. Thousands upon thousands of stars were visible. Planets could be seen, and the sun and moon, too. Beyond it all there were other suns and planets, other universes. They all moved perfectly, precisely, in exact relation to one another. The universes and galaxies and universes beyond them had all become part of a huge mechanism. It was the Universal Time Clock, and it measured Universal Time. He lay back and smiled, for after all he, David Green, was The Universal Timekeeper—or, better yet, Keeper of *the* Time—all Time.

He made sure the cover was tucked about him perfectly. He lay still—and fell asleep, his right hand clutched around the ancient teddy bear ear under his pillow. The light remained on all night.

∞

"John, John, begone, begone—enough, enough of this stuffy stuff."

"Are you angry with me, Lisa?"

"Angry, angry—bangry, wangry,—be gone, John; John, be gone."

"I guess you are angry. What is it that makes you so angry?"

"You foo, you foo—it's you, it's you—it's you, you foo; foo you, foo you."

She suddenly broke into a wild screaming laugh. She screamed and laughed continuously, imperceptibly inhaling air to laugh some more. After five minutes he interrupted her. "You're still angry, aren't you, Lisa?"

She stopped abruptly.

"You louse, louse—John is a louse, a big fat louse on a little gray mouse."

She looked up at the big man and grinned—an inane, foolish kind of grin. Her mood changed suddenly. The expression on her face became one of utmost seriousness. She suddenly charged away from the man and ran to the other side of the large reception room. She faced the wall and talked to herself in a barely audible whisper.

"He won't give me anything. He's big and fat and mean and why won't he give Lisa the crayons? He would give them to Muriel. He likes the Muriel me—but today I'm Lisa me, Lisa me."

Then she broke into a hop-skip-and-a-jump, quickly running around the walls of the room.

"Lisa, Lisa, is my name—today I'm the same—the same—the same, the same."

"May I speak to you, John?"

John turned to the tall, thin, teenage boy. David wore horn-rimmed glasses, was fastidiously dressed in a gray tweed suit, and conveyed the impression of utmost seriousness and dedication to intellectual pursuit. His pinched, thin, white face seemed too small for his long body. He spoke with the utmost precision.

"Why, yes, David. What would you like to say?"

"Thank you for your indulgence. Of late it has become increasingly difficult to find ears for my words. I've been studying your patient, or, since you are not a physician, shall I say student. I have come to several conclusions, which I feel time and further study by your staff will validate. Lisa is schizophrenic and is a child—I would say approximately twelve years of age. Therefore, my diagnosis would be childhood schizophrenia, undoubtedly of the chronic variety. However, diagnostic work is no challenge to me. I prefer to study the dynamic aspect of a particular case. Do you follow me?"

"Yes. Yes, indeed I do." John shook his head affirmatively.

"Good. Then I will continue."

Lisa was still hopping and skipping around the room, now periodically emitting a loud war whoop.

David chose his words carefully, the effort graphically demonstrated by his eyes and mouth. "Lisa has a most difficult time with authority or authoritarian figures. It is therefore extremely important that you adopt an attitude of complete permissiveness in your rela-

78

tionship with her. You must realize that this child has utmost difficulty with her emotions. Now, it is my belief that this difficulty is related to her obsession with speaking in rhymes. The rhyming serves as a decoy or camouflage for what she actually feels. I therefore think that you should not have refused her the crayons, even though she marked the wall."

Lisa stopped skipping and walked over to them.

"John, John, don't be gone—don't be gone."

"I'll see you later, David." He patted David on the shoulder.

The boy lurched away and screamed, "You touched me, you boor, you unmitigated fool—you touched me! Do you want to kill me? A touch can kill—you bastard, you rotten bastard!" His face was contorted with rage. He turned and left them, muttering to himself, "The touch that kills, the touch that kills," and carefully examining his shoulder.

"Can we sit down and talk a while?"

"Dr. White, I submitted to extensive testing, interviewing, and other such nonsense when I first came here, a year ago. I also spoke to you on occasion after that. Somehow I thought I'd go along with the routine here. New place—all right, I'd go along with the indignities. But there's a limit, even to cooperation—and, frankly, I don't care for more interviewing."

"You felt, New place, get off to a new start."

"Well, I suppose you could say that."

"David, it's not more interviewing I'm interested in.

It's talking things over so that perhaps I can help you. After all, that's what we're both here for."

"You call me David—but I call you Dr. White."

"You don't have to."

"What do you mean?"

"You can call me Alan."

"All right, Alan." He smiled. "Let me think about it. When I'm ready, we'll talk."

"Suits me—You know where to find me; I'll be available."

"Suits me too." He walked out of the day room to the library.

She walked to where he was standing and placed herself directly in front of him. She looked up into his eyes and didn't budge. He stared back at her. In a completely serious voice she said, "Hello, hello, kiddo, kiddo."

He smiled. "Kiddo, hello; hello, kiddo."

She felt encouraged—and smiled ever so slightly at him.

"Me, the name; Lisa, the same."

For a minute he was puzzled, but when she repeated, "Me, the name; Lisa, the same," he realized she was asking him a question and then he caught on and answered.

"Me, the same; David, the name."

This time she smiled fully, and it wasn't a silly smile.

∞

She passed David working at his table. On it was a large drawing of a clock.

Then she skipped about the room, chanting in a loud voice.

"Dockety dock, clock, clock; dockety dockety, clock clock clock.

"Hockety clock, dockety hock. Hock, hock; dock, dock."

Then she skipped over to John, who was sitting at the other end of the room. First she just stood in front of him. After a few minutes she slowly rocked from foot to foot. Five minutes later she rocked and chanted, this time in a low voice that only John could hear.

"Rockety rock, clock clock—
dickety—rickety—lock lock."

John started to say something, but she ran off on a tour around the room.

∞

He spent days pouring over books. There were physics books, math texts, engineering manuals, and books on horology. When he wasn't reading, he spent hours at a drawing board, making elaborate plans of watch and clock mechanisms.

Alan made several attempts to discuss his work with him, but David remained seclusive. At times he ignored Alan. At other times he said, "You're not really interested," or, "You wouldn't understand."

Then one day he picked up the plans he had drawn and locked them in his foot locker. From that time, he began to make more frequent visits to the day room.

"Do you have a watch?"

"Yes." He held out his wrist.

"Don't touch me." There was panic in his voice. "Please, don't touch me."

The man let his hand drop back to his side.

"Oh, you can hold your hand up. I'd love to see your watch—but let's not touch." He laughed a small, apprehensive laugh.

The man held his hand up again. David looked at the watch but made sure not to touch the man.

"That's not a very interesting timepiece. Is it the only one you own?"

"I have another, but right now it's not working."

"Oh? What kind is *it?*"

"A small, automatic, waterproof watch. I don't recall the make."

"I see. Probably not very good either. Do you know what kind of eccentric it uses?"

"Eccentric?"

"Yes—the rotor, the winding gear."

"I really don't know."

"Probably on a one-hundred-and-eighty-degree track. The better watches rotate fully, three hundred and sixty degrees."

"I see."

"Do you?" He stared at the man's eyes. "I don't think you do. So few people do. But I'll tell you anyway. There are automatic systems that work by bearings rather than rotor."

"How interesting."

David looked at him skeptically and said, "Perhaps we'll see each other again later; I have to spend a little time observing Lisa now."

"Could I possibly detain you for just a few minutes?"

"Detain me?" He rather liked the expression. "Yes, I suppose I could allow myself to be detained for several minutes."

"Tell me, are you interested in clocks, too?"

"Of course, I'm interested in watches, clocks, sundials—timepieces of all kinds. As a matter of fact, I had my clock execution dream last night."

"Clock execution dream?"

"I thought you would be interested. Frankly, I think you people put too much stress on dreams."

"Oh? Would you tell it to me anyway?"

"Yes, why not? This is a repetitive dream; I've had it time and again. It is always identical; only the characters are different."

"I see."

"No, you don't, but after I tell you, you will see.

"There's a big clock on a spike set in a large white bath tub. The tub is ten times larger than an ordinary one. The hands are huge, exquisitely sharp blades. I sit on a plush perch on the large hand. The face is white enamel. The numerals are sparkling diamonds. The movement is made by Patek Philippe. There are holes throughout the face to accommodate the heads of people sitting on little elevated stools on the other side of the clock. At ten o'clock the execution begins. The large hand, minute by minute, cuts through each neck, cutting off heads. The blood and heads fall into the bathtub."

"Who are the people?"

"They vary. Last night it was John." He pointed to

the big man. "It was John—over and over again John
—eight times. Who knows? Tonight maybe it will be
you."

He walked away whistling.

∞

"Did you analyze my dream—or does it require
further study?"

"Neither."

"Neither?" He was interested now. "Meaning
what?"

"A dream has meaning only in terms of the dream-
er's symbols."

"Sounds like double talk. Did you at least discern
that I was crazy?"

"Crazy?"

"Yes, crazy, or—if you prefer—psychotic—though
there's something vulgar about the word 'psychotic.'
I prefer 'crazy'—more direct and at the same time
homey.

"But what about my dream? You must have thought
about it. Or will you evade my question with either
more double talk or psychiatric gibberish?"

"You sound angry in your dream—cutting off heads
that way. Specifically, you sound angry at John—at
least in the last dream you told me. And you sound
angry now, too."

He laughed a high-pitched, forced laugh full of
mockery. "Brilliant, a brilliant analysis. Killing—hostility—John, anger at John. But how about the fiendish
execution machine—the clock death dealer—the bath-

tub of heads and blood? Surely, surely, you detect the bizarre formulations of paranoid ideation, the intricate workings of a schizophrenic mind."

"Labels never interested me particularly."

"Well, what *does* interest you?"

"People, and what makes them tick."

"People ticking. I like that. Perhaps you *can* understand. I'll tell you an aspect of my clock dream that you did not think of." He waited patiently.

"The second-by-second, minute-by-minute cutting off of heads happens to all of us all of the time. The clock blades represent time, and the victims are all of us; and time slowly, slowly cuts us down—and there is no stopping it—no slowing it. On and on it goes, most accurately and effectively concentrating on batch after batch of victims from the second they are born. There is no escape."

They were silent.

∞

"You said nothing when I interpreted my dream to you yesterday."

"That's right, I said nothing."

"Are you trying to get me angry?"

"No. I will not attempt to manipulate you in any way."

"Thanks," he said acidly.

After a few moments of silence he looked up. "Well, how come you said nothing?"

"Well, what do you think about it?"

"If you have to stay on good terms with me, don't touch me; don't touch me, and don't get Talmudic with me."

"I haven't touched you."

"That's true—but no Talmud, please."

"Stop being cute. You know what I mean. The business of answering a question with another question, this psychiatric, 'Well, what do you think about it?' So how come you *did* say nothing?"

"I wanted to give it some thought."

"Did you?"

"Yes, I did."

Now he spoke in a soft, childlike voice. There even seemed to be a slight tremor in his voice. "Alan, will you tell me *anything?*"

"All right, I will." He chose his words carefully, speaking very slowly. "I think you're afraid of death —terribly afraid."

"Of course, I am. Who isn't?"

"Now *you're* getting Talmudic."

David laughed a full, hearty laugh. Then he spoke. "I know that you know I'm afraid of death. You knew from the start how I can't stand to be touched— but the dream—I'm talking about the dream."

"So am I."

"Oh?" His eyebrow went up.

"Yes, it shows up in two ways. First, you're sitting on the blade killing your enemies—which will make you feel safer. And, secondly, *you're* sitting on the blade—controlling death and life."

"Enough, enough! I've had enough now. I'll see you later." He walked away.

"Sitting here talking to you reminds me of the first time they brought me to a psychiatrist."

"Oh?"

"Yes. You know—my first consultation." He laughed bitterly. "I was ten years old."

"What about it? How did it go?"

"When we got to the house, a big brownstone—just as we got there—a young girl, about eighteen, ran down the stairs—and into the street. A second later a very old, bent, woman came running after her yelling, 'Come back.' But the young girl was way out of her reach. The old lady yelled, and I remember the exact words—'If you don't come back for your shock treatments, they will put you away.' She yelled back, 'Grandma, I'm afraid. I can't. When I'm ready—not now—not now, please.' "

"How'd you feel?"

He ignored the question and went on with the story. "She didn't come back. A little crowd gathered, and they all watched. In no time at all the girl was a block away. The old woman kept chasing her but couldn't possibly catch up. Everybody looked—but nobody helped; they just stood and watched. You know what I think?"

"What?"

"I think everybody wanted to see that girl get away. They were hoping she'd escape."

"Did you?"

"Yes."

"Then what happened?"

"I went in but hardly spoke to the psychiatrist at all. You know what he said?"

"What?"

"That I'd be all right—nothing serious—for them not to worry. An idiot—an M.D. idiot!"

"Are you angry with me, David?"

"What do you mean?"

"Would you like to call me an idiot? Would you like to run from here? You know—like the girl?"

"That's a crazy idea."

"Is it?"

"Well, this place isn't the most fascinating, you know. Anyway, I have to go to the library now."

He got up and left the room.

∞

"Muriel, Muriel is a cigar—just like a car—a car, a car."

She skipped around the room quickly and now changed the rhythm slightly.

"Muriel, Muriel, is a cigar—and it smokes like a car, smokes like a car."

Then she changed to a hop-skip-and-a-jump and changed her rhyme again.

"Hop, skip, jump—Hop, skip, jump. I'm not alump, I'm not alump."

John stepped in front of her. She stopped short.

"No, you're not a lump. You're a girl, Lisa."

She walked around him and resumed skipping.

"I'm not a lump, and I like to jump. Lisa, Lisa is my name—but Muriel, Muriel is the same, the same."

"It's not the time or keeping time that interests me. It is the timepiece itself. The accuracy with which a particular instrument keeps time is directly proportional to the effort and skill of the creator."

"Creator?"

"Yes, creator!"

"Peculiar word to use in connection with a machine."

"I know. You would say 'artisan'—or, worse yet, 'technician'—or even 'mechanic' or 'manufacturer.' "

"Yes, I would."

"Yes, indeed. That is because to you a watch is only a machine used to serve a purpose—to tell time."

"And to you? What is it to you?"

He grinned slyly. "Thank you for asking me. I needed your question as an introduction. The timepiece to me, if it is a master timepiece, is a creation—a creation symbolizing the utmost skill and artistry. Think of the effort and skill involved in creating a clock that is nearly absolutely accurate. Think of the combination of these utterly precise instruments—and I call the clock parts 'instruments'—arranged in an almost perfect pattern for the purpose of harnessing time."

"Harnessing?"

He laughed an almost natural laugh. " 'Harness' is only a figure of speech—a slip." He became serious again. "I should say to measure time. You know—as one measures length, width, and breadth with a micrometer. To measure this, the most important dimension of all, the most dynamic—this ever-moving, ever-changing, and not changing at all—this most terrifying dimension of all—Time. He stopped and then a minute later, almost as an after-thought to himself, said, "If only we *could*, harness time."

"We can."

"We can?" He looked up at Alan, his face a picture of alert curiosity.

"Perhaps we cannot change the time allotted to us—perhaps we cannot add even one extra second to it. But if we use time in our behalf, if in the time of our lives we have freedom of choice—so that we have grown even one iota, in one split second in all the time of times—then we *have* harnessed this dimension."

"That is a difficult thought to digest. I must give it some thought."

"And time?" Alan smiled.

"And time," David repeated. He turned and walked away.

∞

She stopped in front of David, stared at him, then said, "David, David looks at me—but what does he see, what does he see?"

He looked up from the desk. "It's Lisa, Lisa whom I see—staring at me, staring at me."

She smiled at him and came a little closer. He stood up quickly and walked a little distance away. "Don't touch, don't touch—me don't touch. All else will do—but please no such."

She stood still and remained smiling.

"Touch, such—such touch—foolish talking, foolish squawking."

He repeated, "Yes, but—no such, no touch."
She agreed. "No such, no touch."

○○

"You made a friend?"

"Friend? What are you talking about?"

"Lisa. I noticed you talking to her."

"Oh, that. Well, don't get any ideas. My social adjustment or any other psychiatric descriptive nonsense you want to apply just doesn't apply here."

Alan smiled.

"What's so funny?"

"Funny? Oh, nothing funny. I was just thinking that I take great pains not to use so-called psychological technical language, and yet here you accuse me of doing just that anyway."

"All right, that's true," he said grudgingly. "You talk straight enough; it was the others. Does that make you feel better?"

"Yes, it does," Alan said seriously. "It does make me feel better."

"Good for you," David smiled. "Can I get back to this Lisa-child business now?"

"Yes, please do."

"Thank you," he said, clenching his jaw. "Thank you, very much."

Alan remained quiet.

"As I was saying, Lisa is not a friend. I have no friends. If I did have a friend—which is rather inconceivable—it is unlikely that I would choose a twelve- or a thirteen- or fourteen-year-old infant—obviously my intellectual inferior. I talk to Lisa only because she interests me clinically. I would hardly bother to do something arduous and boring as to talk in rhymes for the mere purpose of a ridiculous friendship."

"I see."

"Good."

He walked to the other side of the large day room to wait for Lisa to come down from her own room.

Lisa walked into the day room. Her head was bent, and she walked slowly.

David approached her. He said nothing. John and Alan spoke quietly on the other side of the room.

"Lisa, Lisa, do you want to talk; or would you rather take a walk?"

"Talk, walk. Don't you see—today I'm sick; I'm not me." She walked away and he followed. Her mood seemed to change abruptly. She skipped around the room but said, "Today I'm low, low; so, David, go, go, go." He walked away.

Alan walked to him. "You look angry."

"Angry, bangry," he grinned. "No, I'm not angry. It's just that she's hard to reach."

"Maybe she just doesn't feel well just now."

"I have a feeling that she's trying to tell me that she's menstruating."

"Oh, maybe she is. How do you feel about it?"

"Feel! Is that all you think of—feel, feel? I don't feel. I don't feel a thing. Now what do you feel about that?"

"I feel you're angry. As Lisa would say, 'angry, bangry.'"

"I don't think it's funny, and I don't think you understand Lisa or me. I'm not angry—and I'll tell you what I feel—hungry. Yes, hungry. That's what I feel—hungry." He turned to leave the room.

"Well, feeling hungry is a feeling." But David paid no attention and walked out.

∞

She printed on a white piece of paper with black crayon and then held it up to him. YOU RIME. TALK PLAIN—STRAYT.

"Oh, that makes it easier. It's not s-t-r-a-y-t; it's s-t-r-a-i-g-h-t—and r-h-y-m-e not r-i-m-e."

She printed STRAIGHT and RHYME.

"Can you spell out loud?"

NO, she printed in huge letters.

"All right, all right—nobody is going to force you, Lisa."

NOT LISA—WHO LISA——MURIEL—MURIEL —I—ME—MURIEL.

"Lisa, Muriel. Frankly, I prefer the name Lisa."

She pointed at him with her index finger—and then came a little closer. He backed away, but she followed.

"Lisa, don't touch me. Now be careful, don't touch me!"

She returned to the table and printed MURIEL in huge letters, filling a whole piece of typing paper. She held it up to him.

"Yes—I see. All right, Muriel, Muriel, don't touch me!"

She smiled a little half-smile and returned to the table and sat down.

Lisa and John sat at the table, the paper and pencils before them, saying nothing.

Finally, after some twenty minutes he asked if she would care to write something, or perhaps draw.

She shook her head no. She then walked to the screened window and looked out and watched the clouds. To her it seemed as though they were running after one another in slow motion. After a few minutes she returned to the table, picked up the pencil, and drew three clouds; then she drew them closer together—then overlapping, and finally one cloud within another. She then drew a big black X through them all.

David and Alan came into the room, busily talking in low voices.

Once again she picked up the pencil and printed, DAYVED.

John said, "Very good—very good, indeed."

She printed, DAYVED, again, this time in much larger letters.

John took another sheet of paper and printed, DAVID—DAVID GREEN. "This is another way of spelling his name—the way he spells it. Green, you know, is his second name."

She took a fresh sheet of paper and printed, DAVID GREEN——MURIEL.

She looked up at him and pursed her lips—but it wouldn't come. She couldn't think of her second name. Tears ran down her cheeks.

"Brent," he said "Brent."

She tore the sheet up into little pieces; then took a fresh one and printed:

and then broke into uncontrollable sobbing.

⊙⊙

"Lisa, Lisa, why must we rhyme? It's so hard to do and takes so much time."

"Funny David, can't you see? Rhyming stops her, she then can't be."

He looked up with the surprise of discovery. "That's it, that's it. That's why you rhyme; you suppress Muriel by rhyming. You suppress her—now I see."

She darted away.

"Lisa, I'm sorry. I'll rhyme; yes I will rhyme—slime, climb, rhyme. Lisa, Lisa," he called. But she was away now, far away.

The panic overtook her. She ran around the room quickly.

"Climb, slime, climb, slime—I can't rhyme; oh, I can't rhyme." She began to cry. "I can't rhyme, I can't rhyme."

And a buzz in her head got louder. Then it grew and became a voice. The voice filled her head; it terrified her. And then she became calm. She sat down at the table with John.

"Do you feel better, Lisa?"

She looked up at him and laughed, a deep sarcastic laugh. There was no sound. But its expression was clear on her face.

"Won't you talk?"

Again she laughed the soundless laugh.

"I see, you won't talk." He handed her the sheet of paper.

She drew a huge cigar and colored it bright red. Underneath it she printed:

I AM MURIEL NOW.

∞

"I had a peculiar dream last night."

"Oh? Would you care to tell me about it?"

"Yes, I will tell you. I searched and searched. It was terribly hard. But then I found it—the Lost Continent. It was a vast place and yet it was small. There were only thin, tall people there. They all wore glasses and were immaculately clean and young. Everybody knew that they must not touch each other. I felt that I'd found—well, as if I'd found home."

"You were comfortable there."

"Yes, I was comfortable there," he said softly.

"Everybody in the dream sounds like you—at least from the outward description."

"I suppose you could say that.

"Say, do you think it's because I would like to find a place—that is for me? You know, a place where all the others, the you's, would be strangers."

"That may be," Alan replied gently. "But as you said, the continent was a lost one. Perhaps, David, it would be easier to get to be able to live in this, the world that isn't lost."

"Perhaps, but I don't know." He shook his head as if to clear it. "I mean I'll have to think about it some more."

Lisa's heads poked through the holes. There was only one Lisa sitting on a high stool behind the clock. But she had eight faces, and each of them wore a different expression. One looked silly; another was frightened; the third had a crafty look, and the fourth laughed a high-pitched screaming kind of laugh. He couldn't make out the expressions on the other four but knew that they were all different. Then the sixth from the numeral twelve—and he thought, Twelve noon or twelve midnight—started to talk. "David, David, I'll talk to you, because that is what I like to do." The first face came into focus. It smiled warmly, even tenderly. He thought of his teddy bear—and its soft cloth ear.

Then ten o'clock rang out and the hands started to move. But a funny thing happened. All the heads came into focus, and the faces looked sweet and gentle. And the hands stopped. He yelled, "Go on, go on!" But they wouldn't budge. He pleaded. "Please, go on." But they didn't move. Then he screamed, "Oh, God, my God!"

His screaming woke him. He was drenched in sweat. He felt very stiff. This was followed by an unfamiliar funny feeling, and then he became very frightened. He quickly stuck his hand under the pillow and found the soft ear of the ancient teddy bear. He brushed his nose, then his eyelids, and then his lips with it. It made him feel better.

Before too long he forgot the nightmare and fell asleep.

He sat at the table reading the math book.

She slipped the note on the table and then stood still. He read it.

PLAY WIT ME.

He looked up at her.

With controlled anger he said, "How stupid can you be! It's 'with' not 'wit'—with, with, not wit. Now, go, leave me be."

She turned around and started to walk away—but suddenly turned again and approached him. But she had changed, looked different, and he got up, a little frightened, ready to leave the room.

"Leave me, be me. David, shmavid, shmavid David."

"Play, play another day," he said, trying to placate her.

But she continued bitterly, "David shmavid—shmavid David."

"All right!" He clenched his teeth. "Lisa, shmisa, shmisa, Lisa."

He turned and left the room.

⦿

"Finish squawking and talking. Finish talking and

squawking. Skipping, jumping, jumping, skipping—that's what I want to do.

"David, skip and jump with me, and I'll skip and jump with you."

"I won't skip and I won't jump, but I'll walk while we talk."

"No squawk talk, no talk squawk—but let's walk, let's walk."

They walked around the day room and said nothing. They were careful not to touch each other.

⦾

A nurse told him that Lisa did not feel well and could not come down to the day room. David sat down in an easy chair in one of the small side rooms. After several minutes Alan walked in and sat a short distance from him.

"A penny for your thoughts."

"These are worth considerably less than that."

"I see."

They sat silently for some ten minutes.

"Do you know what I was thinking about when you came in?"

"No, what?"

"Well, just before I came here—that is, to this place —an odd incident occurred."

"Oh, what's that?"

"I had to go uptown to get a clock catalogue. Against my better judgement and with much trepidation, I took the train—the subway. As soon as I got on it, I knew it was a mistake. It looked filthy, but

I had to get uptown—and at least it was almost empty. Well, we came to De Kalb Avenue, and a load of peopled walked in. I wanted to get out—but couldn't without bumping at least one of them—and then the train started, and it was too late. I stood in a corner of the car; I steeled myself but it was no use—I felt very sick. Then we came out of the tunnel, onto the bridge. Being on the bridge made me feel even more closed in—more—well, caught. I had violent palpitations, felt I couldn't breathe." He hesitated and then looked at Alan's eyes. "I guess I thought I'd have a heart attack."

Alan waited, but David didn't go on. He seemed to be daydreaming—away from the room.

"Then what happened?" Alan asked in a whisper.

"Oh, well, that's the funny part of the story—what happened next. And, you know, it all happened within minutes—from the beginning of the Manhattan bridge to Canal Street."

Alan waited.

"It was one of the few times I thought of my mother and father. Suddenly they just occurred to me, and for a second or two I felt better. Then I pictured them yelling at each other, and I felt awful again. That's when the funny thing happened. I saw this woman—a heavy, smiling, Jewish Mamma kind of woman. She was with her three children. There was a boy eighteen, a boy thirteen, and a little boy about six. The little boy was leaning against the thirteen-year-old, sleeping and sucking his thumb. And they were all talking together. Mostly the conversation was about the little boy—how cute he was—Is he still sleeping? Let him sleep, let him sleep—that kind of talk. You know, she didn't have three children; she had four. I became the fourth. I was part of that family—one of her boys—and the funny thing is, the sickness left. I didn't even get off at Canal—I rode right on to Fifty-seventh. Funny, isn't it?" He laughed. "She never knew she had another boy."

"No. I don't think it's funny at all."

His face became serious again. "I'm going to take a walk in the yard now."

"Would you like me along?"

"As you wish."

They got up and left the room.

⚭

He sat with the large physics textbook in front of him. But he didn't look at the material. Periodically he glanced over the top and stared at John and Lisa. They sat at the low table, printing.

That bastard, he thought, that vicious bastard. He'd like to see me dead—I know—I just feel it. I'll watch. I'll watch—touch me, touch me. Probably says vicious things about me. She doesn't understand anyway—how could she—that silly child—that man—a fool, a complete fool—therapist—therapist and he touched me. How he hates me, how he hates—that coarse, stupid, dirty, ridiculous bastard. He doesn't understand that child. Look at the man—big, fat, stupid, vicious, insensitive. Probably wears an American watch—a Mickey Mouse American watch. No accuracy in that man—no precision—clumsy, stupid clumsy. I hate to even look at him.

He got up and stalked out of the room with his physics book.

There was a large clock. It ticked steadily as the hands slowly moved around the face. He stood under the large hand and held it, trying to keep it from moving. But it was too strong and kept going. He hung from it—but it moved with him on it. He threw things at it—it kept moving. He struck it again and again with an ax—but it didn't make a dent. He hit it with the sledge hammer. There was a hollow ring that changed to a laugh. The laughing was like a ticking now, and the laughing-ticking said, "Can't stop me, me me me—can't stop me, me me me." He screamed in his sleep and woke up feeling mixed up. But he quickly got up and in so doing re-established his equilibrium.

He went to the bathroom and showered. He soaped himself scrupulously, accounting for every milimeter of skin surface. He soaped and showered eight times, the entire operation taking an hour and ten minutes. He shaved with utmost care, making absolutely certain that no hair remained on his face. After urinating and defecating, he washed his hands six times, brushed his teeth three times, and then carefully combed his hair, making sure that the part was perfectly straight. His entire bathroom activity took two hours, but he had plenty of time until breakfast. After he finished dressing, it was only seven thirty.

She looked at herself in the mirror. The girl who looked back at her seemed indistinct, blurred. She tried to make her more real, but she still looked wispy, faded, as if she would disappear. Then she tried to make her more real by making silly faces. She blew her cheeks up with air. She stuck her tongue out. She smiled foolishly. Nothing worked; the image was still vague. Then she clenched her teeth and curled her lip; an angry face looked back at her—but it looked real, of substance, alive. But the anger in it scared her. She turned away from the mirror—and was out of the room, away from the hateful face.

For several days she didn't dare look at the mirror in her room.

She lay in bed and looked up at the ceiling. A little light came through the shaded window. She could just make out a vague shadow on the ceiling. She put her hand on her face. Then her hand seemed to be separated from the rest of her. It was as if it had a life of its own. She regarded it in a detached way—but at the same time concentrated on it so that it absorbed her completely.

It lightly touched her hair and mussed it up in an almost affectionate way. Then it traced the outlines of her nose and mouth almost as a blind person would. Then it came down to her neck and clenched it tightly. At the same time, she felt a kind of bubbling laughing in her head and got frightened. Then she grasped her right hand with her left and removed it from her neck. It moved downward. It touched her small breasts and nipples, and this felt pleasant. Then it went over her belly to her thighs, to her clitoris. It rubbed her clitoris, and it felt nice. After a while fear and tension was almost gone, and she fell asleep. When she woke in the morning, her hand was part of the rest of her again.

∞

He lay in bed, and at first he didn't sleep. Then he had a fantasy. After a while the fantasy slipped into a dream as he finally fell asleep. There was a great clock—a huge precision instrument made up of extremely complicated parts. It read four o'clock, and chimes rang out four o'clock. Then a voice—neither male nor female, a metallic voice—said, "It's four—one, two, three, four o'clock." Then the clock stopped. It would go no further. Then for an important reason he added twelve to the four and it added up to sixteen. But the clock still didn't move. After a while the clock turned back to 1 again, and this time went to sixteen o'clock. But it stopped short at 16 and would go no further. The clock then turned into the most complicated mechanism possible. It was an electronic, atomic clock. It was very strong. But it could not break through 16. He then had a funny sensation. Half of him felt different from the other half. It was as if an invisible line was drawn through the middle of him, dividing him into two hemispheres. He looked back at the clock. It was trying desperately to move past 16. It seemed to move past—a second and a half past—and then he stopped dreaming.

When he woke, he had a fleeting thought—he was

trying to charge through a concrete wall but made
no impression on the smooth hard surface.

He spoke to Alan later that day.

"Do you know anything about electronic clocks?"

"No—but sounds interesting."

"I'm sixteen today."

"Oh! Happy birthday."

"About that talk we had——"

"Which?"

"You know, some time ago. Controlling time."

"Oh, yes. What about it?"

"This business of choice. If you have a choice over
the time, you said."

"What about it?"

A look of disgust came over his face. "Stop this
pedantic what-about-it stuff! I'm asking you about it.
It's your production, so can you spare a few words to
elaborate on it?"

"Choice means just that—choice. When people are
not well, much of what they do is done because they
have to do it. But if they get better and become
themselves, then they are free to do as they please;
they have a choice."

"You mean compulsive versus noncompulsive."

"You could say that—though I prefer to use plain
language rather than technical terms."

"Thanks for being so condescending. Also thanks
for the 'they' routine—when you mean me." He suddenly got angry. "Me! That's right, me. Me—David.
Real compulsive nut—aren't I?"

Alan started to answer, but David suddenly got
up and walked away.

"David, David, here you are; come with me far, oh far." She looked up at him beseechingly.

"Not today, not today—tomorrow I say, tomorrow I say." He walked to Alan's office. The door was open.

"Hello, David. Please come in."

"She irritates me—certainly can be a nuisance."

"She?"

"That Lisa child."

"She annoys you?"

"Well, sometimes she—oh, I don't know. It's like—oh!" He threw his hands up in exasperation.

"Everybody is irritated at times."

"Is that supposed to make me feel better?"

"Better or worse—it's simply a statement of fact."

"Statement of fact—I like that. Well, I'll tell you a fact. I had a really crazy dream last night; a real . . ." He looked for the words but couldn't find them.

"A real lulu."

"Yes." He smiled. "Could say that—a real lulu. You want to hear it?"

"Sure do."

"I had a funny feeling in my stomach and then the feeling turned to a pain—a gnawing kind of pain. Then in my dream while I had the pain I had a fantasy at the same time. The fantasy involved my having a rat in my belly—which was slowly but methodically eating through my diaphragm trying to get to my heart. The next thing, my fantasy changed: instead of a rat, there she was—that ridiculous Lisa child. And her face—that sweet insipid smile of hers."

He waited. Alan said nothing.

"Aren't you going to say anything?"

"Do you want me to?"

"I don't care. But—if you want to—go ahead."

"I think Lisa is getting to you."

"Getting to me?"

"Yes, getting to your feelings. Perhaps you're beginning to like her."

"Like her! How ridiculous can you get!" He spoke between clenched teeth. "She's a clinical study—only clinical. Sometimes you sure can be ridiculous." He got up and left the room—muttering, "So ridiculous, so ridiculous; almost as stupid as that bastard John."

He ran faster and faster but knew that it was not fast enough. He had a pain in his side and was out of breath but kept running. The thought flashed through his mind that he should have been more of an athlete. But is was too late now. He kept running, and the pain in his side now extended itself to his chest. It became unbearable, but he had to keep going. He looked down. It was there all right, and he couldn't jump to the side. He could run, but some kind of magnetic pull kept him glued to the treadmill. But it wasn't a treadmill; it was a clock, a linear clock. It was a ribbon of ever-moving time that kept disappearing into a huge abyss of nothing. He ran counterclockwise, but time ran out a little faster—and every second brought him closer to the nothingness. Then he realized that running served no purpose; he could not escape the movement of time. And then he was in the nothingness—falling; falling through space—and there was a clock in his head that ticked off the seconds; time was running out, fast. He would soon become part of the nothingness. The ticking stopped—and he woke.

For several days he spoke to nobody. He went to meals and spent the rest of the time reading books and drawing plans of elaborate clocks. He did not return Alan's greeting.

Then one day, after nearly a week had passed, he returned to the day room. Alan walked up to him.

"Good to see you back, David."

"Good! You mean good for you. You like winning, don't you?"

"Winning?"

"You know what I mean. Winning—between us. Me being here again."

"I didn't know we were having a battle. As a matter of fact, I consider us both on the same side—your side."

"My side?"

"Yes, your side—to help you. After all, that's what I'm here for."

"Sounds corny."

"What does? That anybody should want to help you?"

"That's enough of this psychology. Let's talk of other things."

"Suits me."

"Alan, have you ever considered the possibility of a radio clock?"

"You mean a radio alarm?"

"No, no. That's just a gadget everybody has. I mean —well, this is a new idea. You wouldn't say anything; I mean, I want secrecy—absolute secrecy."

"Everything you tell me is confidential."

"Well, people would wear this clock receiver which would be timed in to a central electronic device—through which they would constantly be informed of the exact time."

"If they were interested."

"What do you mean?"

"Well, I think the idea shows much ingenuity—but few people are interested in constantly having the exact time."

He did not answer and just sat still.

After a few minutes Alan asked, "Have I offended you. David?"

"No."

"David, what made you so angry? You didn't talk to me for about a week."

"It was my feeling."

"Yes, what feeling?"

"I felt you and John were talking about me—that he said vicious things about me. Did—I mean, did he?"

"No."

"No?"

"No."

"The feeling was very strong."

"Your feeling about John must be very strong."

"I hate him! He's an uncouth, savage, ridiculous idiot. I don't see how he'll ever help that child."

"Lisa?"

"Yes, Lisa. What time is it?"

"Ten minutes to lunch time." Alan smiled. "David, how come you own no watch?"

"There isn't a timepiece made that interests me. They're grossly inaccurate—clumsy junk. I don't like them next to my skin. Some day, when I make one—

a real piece—a masterpiece—then I'll carry it. It won't be a wrist watch anyway."

"Oh? Why not?"

"They can never be really accurate. Besides, I don't like to constrict my wrist. I'm hungry."

"Good. Just about time for lunch."

"I've been thinking about this business of Lisa getting to me."

"Yes."

"Well, she is a rather interesting child."

"Interesting?"

"Well, there are times she—well—when her face is interesting-looking."

"She is nice-looking. Beautiful eyes."

"Nice, beautiful—I didn't say that."

"No, you didn't. I did."

"She does have expressive eyes."

"I think so."

"But she can be silly."

"Silly?"

"Well, this jumping about—rhyming and the rest."

"Perhaps she can't help herself?"

"Perhaps? There's no perhaps about it. You know very well she can't help herself. After all, she is a sick child."

"Yes, I agree."

OO

FOURTEEN AND A HALF
FOURTEEN YEARS—AND SIX—MONTHS

"Very good—very good, indeed. That's how old you are now—well, to be exact, a week ago."

YOU—YOU, she printed.

"Me?" he said. "If you want to know how old I am, print the question and end with a question mark."

HOW OLD ARE YOU?

"I am sixteen and a half years old—sixteen years and six months."

JOHN, HOW OLD IS HE?

"Frankly, I don't know and I don't care. But I would judge about three—no, maybe only two."

ALAN—ALAN?

"I don't know—perhaps forty or forty-five or so."

A week later she spoke to John.

"You're three, three, three; you see, you see.

Maybe two, two.

Poor you, poor you."

⦾

"I notice you ignore all the other people here."

"Your observation is correct."

"Do you ever have any desire to socialize with any of them?"

"Socialize—that's quite a word to use for a place like this."

"How so?"

" 'Socialize' implies freedom of choice with whom you have social contact. You should know about the phrase 'freedom of choice,' since you are always using it."

"Always?"

"Almost. Not always—sometimes. Anyway, since talking with people must only be with people here—

how much freedom can there be in such a social selection?"

"You can freely choose from the people here."

"Thanks, but no thanks. There's no freedom in that—and you know it. It's like—well, like asking about an opinion of Republican policy among an all-Democratic group. Besides which, there's another implication that I sense."

"What's that?"

"Well, it's that even though we here in this institution are all individuals and as such different, being here, having the same problems, ought to make us enough the same—that is, people think we ought to be enough the same—so as to give us the desire to socialize. Let me tell you I am not the same. None of us are. We may be here—but we're still different."

"I'm glad you recognize that everyone is different, because we all are different. As for problems, everybody has them—in and out of here. But sounds to me as though you're protesting too much—reacting too strongly."

"What do you mean?"

"Well, like being here does in fact make you the same as everyone else—and that talking to them will add to the similarity, and as such is dangerous."

"I don't know what you're talking about. Besides, I have some research to do now." He left for the library.

Three days later he returned another patient's greeting and later on beat him in a game of chess.

She sat in the corner of the room and said in a loud, clear voice,

"Holly, golly—golly, holly. Golly, holly—holly, golly."

When John approached her, she stopped talking. As soon as he left, she began and repeated over and over again,

"Holly, golly—golly, holly. Golly, holly—holly, golly."

A week later the room was stripped of Christmas decorations.

The snow lasted more than an hour. They searched all over and couldn't find her.

Then John discovered her hiding place. She was in his coat closet. She stood perfectly still inside the heavy tweed coat, using it as a tent. When she came out, the snow had stopped. She skipped and jumped around the room yelling, "Snow, snow, go, go. Go, go—snow, snow."

John spoke to her. "Were you afraid, Lisa? Were you afraid of the snow?"

But she paid no attention and continued to jump about the room.

"Go, go—snow, snow. Snow, snow—go, go."

Then it began again, and she ran for the closet.

This time he put a little stool in the tent, and she sat on it until the snow stopped.

She went to the new poster on the wall and looked at it. It was from a travel agency and pictured a beautiful green farm scene with snow-capped mountains in the background. John came up beside her.

She turned to him and said, "So green, so nice—no snow, no ice."

"Yes, Lisa. Green and nice—no snow, no ice," he repeated back to her.

She went to the table near the window, sat down, and drew on a large white sheet of paper. John sat next to her and watched. When she finished, there was a fairly good replica of the poster in miniature. They took it to the wall and tacked it up next to its parent poster.

She stood back and looked—then said, "No snow, no ice—green and nice."

That night in bed she spoke to herself. "Green grass—tall, warm, green grass." She pictured herself putting her face into it. It was warm and tickled. After a while she fell asleep.

◍

"A page to write my age—to write my age, I need a page." She skipped about the room slowly, repeating again and again, "A page, a page to write my age—to write my age, I need a page."

John stood in her path, and she stopped short. "Here,

Lisa. Here is a piece of paper and a pencil—a page to write your age."

She sat down at the table and printed,

I HAVE A PAGE TO WRITE MY AGE— I'M FOURTEEN AND A HALF THATS NO LAFF.

She looked up at him and smiled. It wasn't a silly smile.

David walked over to her and said nothing. She went to one of the tables and sat down. He sat opposite her. She printed on the pad,

LET US SIT AND TAUK.

"You mean let us sit and talk and write, and talk is spelled t-a-l-k."

YOU PLAY GAME BOY. She pointed to the other side of the room.

"Yes, I played a game of chess with the boy—with Robert."

Her face crackled into a silly grin. She got up and skipped away from him.

"Game, game—boy, poy—chess, chess; mess, mess."

She paid no more attention to him that day.

∞

"Do people really change, Alan? Or I should say, can people change?"

"Yes, I believe they can, and I believe they do."

"I don't know. It's easy to say. You're so glib about it."

"It is easy to say, but that doesn't make it less true. People change; people grow!"

115

"Words, words—just words."

"No, not just words. People change. Look at Lisa."

"Lisa?"

"Yes, Lisa. She writes more, her speech makes more sense—she certainly has improved her relationships here."

"Relationships?"

"Well, like with you. She's friendlier."

"Big change," he grunted.

"Little changes can be important. Growth is a slow process. It doesn't happen suddenly—it's really hard work."

"Hard work, slow process. Funny, I just remembered something."

"Oh? What?"

"When I was very young—maybe seven or eight— two things happened the same day. Completely unimportant—but I never forgot them. About once every year or so I remember them."

"Yes. What were they?"

"If this is psychotherapy, I don't know how it helps —and yet . . ."

"Yet what?"

"Well, I do like to talk—when I'm in the mood. Alan, do you think—well—me here, I mean . . ."

"Yes, you're changing too, David. And I guess I am also."

"Well, anyway, what I remembered was this. My mother and I were on the train going from Brooklyn to Manhattan. We sat near the door. We were both afraid of not being able to get out on time when we'd get to our station."

"Did she say she was afraid?"

"No, but she was; I just knew it."

"I'm sorry for interrupting your story."

"That's O.K." He smiled. "Anyway, on Atlantic

Avenue a very old lady got on the train. She was very thin and dressed poorly, but she kept smiling all the time. As thin and poor as she was, she seemed happy. Anyway, I then noticed she had a package. She sat down next to a heavy, well-dressed woman and then opened the package. She took out three dolls. They were small but exquisite dolls; each feature was perfect, and they were very elaborately dressed. She fussed with each one—straightening the dress, fixing the hair— and all the time smiling and happy. The next thing, the woman next to her started a conversation with her, and in a few minutes I saw her hand the old lady some money and take one of the dolls—a dark one. Then the old lady moved to another seat next to another well-dressed woman and started fussing with the dolls again."

"Did she sell another one?"

"I don't know. We got to our station about then. Well, when we got out and walked a while—the second thing happened that I never forgot."

"What's that?"

"We came to this nice quiet street, and there was a woman cooing and kissing and patting and cuddling a baby in a carriage. When I got up close, I looked at the baby. It was deformed. I don't remember now —but it was abnormal; even it's face wasn't right. But she didn't seem to know about it. She just went on kissing and loving that baby. I thought about it a lot that night. Couldn't sleep—that and other nights."

"Where were you going with your mother that day?"

"I don't remember—but it was probably to the doctor."

"The doctor?"

"Yes. Around that time they kept taking me to the doctors. I was too tall, too thin, underdeveloped—

all kinds of faults." He looked into Alan's eyes. "You know something?"

"Yes?"

"They really were stupid. There's Lisa. I'll see you later."

◌◌

"You know, I haven't had a clock dream in about a month."

"In a month, you say?"

"That's right—at least that."

"I noticed you playing chess."

"Yes, I've been playing with Robert Salkin. Not a bad player—but not much competition. I always win."

"Oh."

"You know something I observed?"

"What's that?"

"I think Lisa gets irritated when I play with Robert." He shrugged his shoulders. "Part of her sickness, I guess."

◌◌

"David, David, look at me—who do you see, who do you see?" She looked up at him questioningly.

He observed her in a clinical, detached way, as he would a clock or a watch, but said nothing.

"David, David—say to me; say to me what you see."

After she repeated the rhyme some ten times, he finally answered. "A girl, a girl—I see a girl. Who looks like a pearl—a small black pearl."

"A girl, a girl—a small black pearl. Girl, pearl; pearl, girl.

"Pearl, girl; girl, pearl. I'm a girl, a pearl—a black girl pearl."

She ran to the other side of the room.

"John, John—I'm a girl, a girl—a pearl of a girl."

David sat by himself at the table thinking of rhymes. It was more difficult than he had anticipated, and such silly things came up: Come away with me—just you and me—away, far away, to a distant sea.

Then he changed it: Come away with me to a distant sea, a distant sea.

Then he thought, slime, slime—climb, chime, dime dime—girl, pearl, pearl girl. A distant land—foreign sand—no touching with a filthy hand. Lisa, Lisa, name the same—enough, enough of this stuffy stuff—stuffy stuff.

He smiled to himself. Enough of this stuffy stuff, indeed—enough of this nonsense.

He got up and went to the library. For a while he sat and did nothing. Then for over two hours he drew an elaborate plan of a clock. It was a precision instrument capable of nearly absolute accuracy. But it didn't satisfy him. He turned it over and drew the face. When he finished the numerals, he recognized the execution machine. He quickly tore it up and threw it into the wastebasket.

She lay in bed and thought about the snow. It seemed so gray and strange and cold. She pictured the sky opening up and tons of it falling down all at once. She pulled the cover over her head, shutting out the little light that came through the shaded window. She remembered the smell of John's coat. Remembering the tweediness of it almost made her sneeze. After a while thoughts of the snow disappeared, and she felt better. After much tossing and turning—so that the bed looked like the scene of a great upheaval—she fell asleep, curled up at the foot of it, the cover over her head.

The dream was one of the few clear ones she ever had. There was a great snow storm and she had to get to the other side of the huge square. She couldn't move. Then she saw John's coat—it was very long and stretched clean across the square. She still couldn't move. Then she saw David on the other side—beckoning to her—and she heard his voice calling, "Lisa, Lisa, Lisa, Lisa——" She stepped on the coat.

When she woke in the morning and looked out the window, she saw the sun, bright and warm.

It was a lovely spring day.

John and Lisa sat together at the large round table in his office. She looked through the magazine, slowly turning the pages and studying the pictures. John read the newspaper. But then she looked up at him and pointed to the white sheet of paper.

She had printed,

HERE DAVID——→

She then took the piece of paper and held it so that the arrow pointed to the magazine picture of a tall blond boy.

John smiled and said, "It does look like him. Yes, it does, Lisa."

She snatched the paper back, turned it over and printed,
MURIEL
MURIEL
She then gave it back to John.
"All right, Muriel."
She took the piece of paper back and printed,
MURIEL—LISA—MURIEL. She smiled at him.
He said nothing and smiled back.

○○

"A clock is to tell time. You know, twelve o'clock, two —Say, do you know about numbers? Did they teach you about numbers in that school?"

She wrote, 1 2 3 4 5.

"That's right. Very good—very good, indeed. You apparently know more than you let on."

David spent the next half-hour drawing clock faces and teaching her how to tell time. Even he was surprised at the rapidity with which she learned. However, when he became philosophical about time, telling about it as a dimension and discussing its importance, she lost interest and no longer paid attention. After a while she left, to look for John. When she found him, she drew clocks for him and demonstrated her newfound knowledge.

David went off to play chess but couldn't find the boy he had played with. He went to Alan's office and told him that he couldn't find his chess partner. Alan suggested that they play a game together, and they did. After the sixth move it became apparent that David was in control of the game.

"Are you letting me win?"

"Letting you? Indeed not."

"Are you sure? You know, part of the therapeutic approach—Getting-to-know-you-better kind of rot—plus, Make the kid feel good."

"You are suspicious; but let me tell you, as I did once before, I have not and will not manipulate you in any way whatsoever."

"I don't know about me being suspicious. But it seems—well, you're not playing too well."

"Now let's get this straight. I play chess with you as I would with anybody. I have too much respect for you to play down in any way. I am playing my best. Did it ever occur to you that you're just a better chess player than I am?"

David smiled. "Me better than you? Well, seems funny."

"Doesn't seem funny to me. I may be older and more expert in psychiatry—after all, I've studied it for years—but you undoubtedly are better versed in other things than I am."

"You're trying to make me feel good."

"Not at all. If you feel good, I'm glad for you. But I am simply stating a fact. The fact is you know more about physics than I do, certainly more about horology. I know more medicine—more psychiatry. All of us, you know, have different assets, abilities, and educations."

"Let's play chess."

"OK."

They made two more moves. David now had him in an impossible position. Another move and Alan would be set up for the checkmate.

David got up. "Well, that's enough. Have some work to do in the library."

"Just a minute." Alan reached up.

"Don't touch me!"

"I won't—but we're close to the end; why not finish?"

"What for? It's—well, it's late."

"David, are you afraid—afraid of beating me? We'll still be friends, you know. It's only a chess game. I've lost before."

He sat down and said nothing. In two more moves he mated him.

"Good game, David. I really enjoyed it."

"But you lost."

"I would get a kick out of winning—but you know something?—the real kick is in playing—especially with a good player who can teach me a thing or two. Now, how about some lunch?"

"I am hungry."

They left for the dining room—together.

∞

MURIEL MURIEL MURIEL, she printed.

"What about Muriel?" John asked.

MURIEL MURIEL

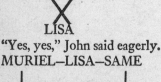

"Yes, yes," John said eagerly.

MURIEL—LISA—SAME

"Yes. All you—that's true."

But she got up and ran off to the other side of the room.

For a minute she stared at Alan and David, who were talking, but then got bored and went to look at some magazines.

∞

"Clocks are more interesting than people."

"How so?"

"They're more accurate, more predictable, and just plain more interesting."

"They're more intricate."

"Clocks?"

"No, people."

"Well, I don't know. Some of these timepieces—but —" He smiled. "Yes, I must admit the human mechanism is more complicated."

"It is—but that's largely because it is not a mechanism. It is not an it; it is a he or she—a person."

"A person. So—what are you getting at?"

"A person. You're right—not predictable because not mechanical. A person—human."

"Human? What's 'human' supposed to encompass?"

"Well—human being—feeling—changing and being unpredictable."

"What's so hot about that?"

"Hot, cold—we are what we are—humans, not clocks."

"A clock is still easier to cope with."

"David, perhaps you are afraid of people?"

"Afraid of people? I suppose so—and perhaps with good reason, too!"

"When you trust yourself more, you'll be less afraid of other people, too."

"Words—just words."

"I don't think so."

He got up and went to his room. He studied the clock plans—but kept thinking of the conversation he had with Alan.

A week later he sat with Alan. For a while he said nothing, but after about ten minutes he spoke.

"I thought about it."

"About what?"

"Me. You know, being afraid of people."

"Yes."

"Well, I think—well, I am afraid—but I'm still interested in clocks and time and things."

"They're not mutually exclusive."

"Meaning what?"

"Meaning, you can still be interested in clocks—just for their own sake."

"But what about death?"

"What about it?"

"Well, I admit it—I'm afraid of it."

"Must be a relief to admit it."

"Yes, I think it is. But isn't everyone afraid of it?"

"Not everyone—but lots of people—to a lesser or greater degree."

"Lesser, greater?"

"Well, my feeling is that people who are afraid to live are afraid to die."

"You mean, if you do a lot of living—then you haven't missed much when you die."

"More or less."

"You know, I just remembered something."

"What's that?"

"I remember going into a movie. I was thirteen years old; it was a bright, sunny day. The movie was dark, pitch black. I found a seat—away—away from everybody. I sat and watched the movie for a while. Suddenly I had a terrible feeling; I broke into a sweat—my heart beat wildly. What I thought of was being dead—the world being there and me gone. The feeling was awful; I felt like I was losing myself—like I was disappearing. Then I ran out of the blackness of the movie into the sunlight. As soon as I got out into the light I felt better."

"You hadn't disappeared."

"No," he said solemnly. "I was still there."

"What were you watching when the fright began?"

"I don't know. You know, I thought about it many times but could never remember. It's funny—my memory is nearly perfect—but that—I couldn't remember."

"I see."

"I'll tell you something I do remember."

"What's that?"

"Well—about a year after that movie incident—I figured something out."

"Yes?"

"I figured out that in a way we never die at all."

"How's that?"

"Well, if people have children and children have children—in a way we go on living just like the branches of a tree."

"It's a very interesting thought."

"Interesting? Well, I don't know. But this I know: at times thinking about it in this way makes me feel lots better."

"Good."

"There's Lisa; I'll see you later."

"OK."

"What do you think about what I told you last week?"

"What are you referring to?"

"Oh, you know—my fears. You know, all that pathology."

"Pathology?"

"Yes—my being afraid of death, and of people."

"Well, its being pathological or nonpathological is not terribly important."

"Not important! It's important enough to be keeping me here."

"While that's true, I'm still not terribly interested in your fears pathologically. Setting judgments—sick, sicker; pathological—it's not too important."

"Then what is?"

"Your fears are symptoms—and also symbols. As such they have value—value as routes to what it is that generated them in the first place."

"I see."

"Do you?" Alan smiled.

"Yes, I think I do—but—well, you're so bland. So—well, isn't it unusual to be so accepting of such sickness—of being crazy?"

"Bland, unusual—words, only words. This I can tell you: only by accepting our difficulties can we use them to better understand ourselves—and to grow healthier. Calling ourselves names—crazy and so forth—it just doesn't serve any purpose."

"Healthier, that's a laugh."

"No, it's not a laugh. Let me tell you, everybody—no matter how sick—also has much health, too."

"You mean a combination?"

"Exactly."

"Even me?"

"Most certainly you."

"You know, it just occurred to me."

"What's that?"

"Your name and mine are colors. Alan White, David Green—White and Green."

"That's true; I hadn't thought of it either."

They sat a while and said nothing. After five minutes, David spoke. "The other day there was something I remembered that I wanted to tell you."

"Oh?"

"Yes. I sat here with you and kept thinking about it —but couldn't talk about it."

"Oh, that will happen—and perhaps one day, when you're ready, you'll talk about it."

That night before he went to bed he thought about it again.

He was eleven and went to a freak show. He saw a boy who was supposed to be turning into an elephant but that didn't bother him. Then he saw a man who put needles through his skin, and he didn't like that at all. At another platform he saw a dwarfed, hunch-backed man billed as "The Human Frog," and he felt terribly sorry for him. Then he came to Alan-Adele—half-man, half-woman. He looked, fascinated—one side bearded, the other side smooth-shaved; flat-chested and full-breasted; long hair, short hair. Then he made the error; he thought of himself. He became terrified and ran out of the show shaking and sweating. He still felt odd when he thought about it. But he couldn't talk about the memory to anybody. Not yet.

128

He decided to try it. He would not rhyme; he would talk to her straight. He sat in the day room in a large rocking chair. A few other patients came in and walked about, but they ignored each other. John came in and said, "Hello," but David did not reply. It was raining outside, a heavy spring rain, but the room was large and bright, well lighted, with many pictures. He looked out the window, at the rain—and the picture of a big beach umbrella popped into his mind. Then he thought of his mother's diaphragm. It was well hidden, and he came across it by accident. He had heard about condoms and thought this was one. It had been in one of their secret places. He didn't touch it—just looked. It seemed all rolled up. But its diameter, its circumference, was huge. He would never grow into the size of that. He remembered running out of the room.

Just then Lisa came in. She immediately walked over to him. John sat at the other side of the room and read the newspaper.

"David, David, how are you? It's raining out—what shall we do?"

"It would have been nice to walk in the garden. But we will do it another time. Come sit down in the chair —over here." He pointed at the other rocker.

She looked at him quizzically. She had rhymed—and he hadn't.

"Chair, there," she whispered, and sat down.

"Lisa, it's hard for me to rhyme. Listen to me—even if it's plain—straight. Lisa, stay." He spoke very slowly and carefully. Now he hesitated—then said, "Lisa, trust me."

She looked up into his eyes. She looked startled and afraid. Then she said in a deeper voice than usual, "David, David, your face is nice; soft, soft—not like snow, not like ice."

He smiled. They sat in the room and rocked up and back in the chairs.

∞

"David, hello, you look nice."

"So do you, Lisa."

"Today I'm fifteen David—fifteen. Let's go and look out the window."

"Happy birthday, Lisa. Lisa, you're not talking in rhymes." His heart beat wildly; then he whispered, "And you're not writing. You're you—Lisa, not Muriel."

"Lisa, Muriel, different, the same—just names. Let's look out the window."

He became very pale and he trembled and his breathing became quicker and deeper. "Lisa." He swallowed hard. "Lisa, take my hand."

She looked up into his eyes and slowly took his hand.

He stiffened and felt a surge of fright course from his hand through the rest of his body. He clenched his teeth and tears ran down his cheeks, but he hadn't died.

Hand in hand, they walked to the window.

Notes

Lisa Brent

INITIAL INTAKE NOTE   *September 15, 1958*

This thirteen-year-old white girl initially appears about two or three years younger than her stated age. Physical examination, however, reveals a normally developed thirteen-year-old, menarche having commenced at age eleven.

Age—13	Skin reveals no stigmata.
Height—5′ 4″	Eye, ear, nose, and throat are
Weight—98	normal.
Blood pressure—100/70	Heart, lungs, and abdomen
Pulse—76	are normal.
Respiration—Normal	Extremities are normal.
Temperature—98.7	Urine Analysis—Negative
Blood Study—Negative	Chest X-Ray—Normal

Neuromuscular reflexes are slightly exaggerated but are within normal limits. Neurologic examination—including response to light, touch, heat, cold, pain; hearing, seeing; and fundi examination—is negative.

In conclusion, there is no evidence of system pathology. Neurologic, respiratory, circulatory, digestive, and urinary examination reveals no demonstrable lesion.

PSYCHIATRIC EXAMINATION: Lisa is a tall, thin, dark-complexioned child. Her eyes are large and light brown; her nose is short and straight. She has a small mouth and even white teeth. Her straight brown hair is parted on the side and is usually disheveled and occasionally neat. Lisa's expression, appearance, and the impression she makes are more than ordinarily linked to fluctuations in her mood and personality. She is about four-fifths of the time a pixie-looking, eye-darting, disorganized, hyperactive four-year-old. She darts about the room, hopping, skipping, and jumping —at times in a dystonic fashion, feet and arms disorganized and going in all directions, and at other times skipping and jumping with the precision of a practiced athlete. In this identity she calls herself Lisa, fluctuates from poor to fair contact, and speaks only in rhymes—in a high, sing-song, infantile voice. Occasionally she moves about in a sluggish fashion, appearing depressed. During these usually brief periods her eyes change from a darting near-squint to a wide-eyed expression of dreaminess and pathos. The observer was surprised during observation of the first of the latter moods at the unusual size of her eyes.

About one-fifth of the time Lisa's identity, mood, and activity become radically changed. Her psycho-motor activity becomes markedly reduced. She walks about in ladylike fashion, almost gracefully. The pixie quality disappears, as does the affective impression of seeming to be a very young child. There is no longer evidence of giggling and silliness. Lisa then appears to be her stated age. However, she no longer calls herself Lisa. At this time she becomes "Muriel," a name which often comes up in her rhymes as Lisa. During the Muriel identification the patient is mute, but she can write, a skill learned in the A——School prior to her admission here. When given pencil and paper, she may or may not print a few words. Her printing and language are surprisingly good, but we feel that she has even better potential. As Lisa, she is aware of her Muriel characteristics. We suspect that she is aware of Lisa as Muriel—but not as aware. Is it possible that her antics as Lisa embarrass her?

There is undoubtedly considerable autistic preoccupation, but at present it is not possible to expose or to evaluate it.

Attention span is extremely poor, making testing almost impossible. From her rhyming productions, however, we can ascertain good orientation in place and person (Lisa/Muriel). We cannot evaluate her orientation in time. From her rhymes, printing, and previous testing we suspect the existence of a superior I.Q. and considerable talent. There are no demonstrable hallucinatory experiences; however, their existence would not be surprising. Aside from the Muriel delusion and preoccupation, there is no evidence of delusional production.

From observation and the small amount of testing possible, we discern much underlying anxiety. To ward off panic attacks, which occur infrequently, she obviously defends herself with hyperactivity, rhyming, disassociation, and mutism. The hyperactivity probably serves to rid her of the excess energy of her anxiety. The rhyming may be a way of repressing certain affects by a veneer of silliness or nursery-rhyming activity but at the same time managing to communicate. Now these affects may be bound up in the compartment labeled "Muriel." The mutism of Muriel may be a last-ditch attempt to repress threatening displays of unwanted feelings. Of course, the latter explanations are only speculations which will or will not be substantiated only after much time has passed.

From the history and the small amount of testing

and contact possible, we feel that Lisa is having much difficulty with the upsurge of sexual feeling and affect in general, particularly anger. Her sickness is essentially an attempt to cope with the latter uncontrollable feelings.

DIAGNOSTIC DISCUSSION: The patient projects a general feeling characteristic of hebephrenia. The giggling, silliness, autistic preoccupation, and affective display of a much younger age level—all contribute to that picture.

However, while her rhymes are sometimes irrational and characteristic of a thought disorder, they are more often rational and indicate a relatively good ability to communicate. There is seldom evidence of a word salad. This, plus the presence of a disassociative process, detracts from that diagnosis.

Suffice to say, then, that the patient is a very sick little girl presenting elements characteristic of hebephrenic schizophrenia complicated by an ability to disassociate, characteristic of multiple personality.

PROGNOSIS: Very serious in view of present findings and their duration, which is dated from at least age six.

RECOMMENDATION: Continuous relating treatment with a therapist—not necessarily a psychiatrist—and maximum freedom, including mixing with one or two other children in the day room.

SIX-MONTH INTERVAL NOTE *March 15, 1959*

The patient's relationship to her therapist and to other patients remains completely superficial and paltry. There have been no changes in her productions or general behavior pattern.

No discernible progress can be noted.

SIX-MONTH INTERVAL NOTE

September 15, 1959

The patient is beginning to relate simultaneously to another patient—David Green—and to her therapist. Her rhyming productions are directed toward them, as is a considerable portion of her interest. There is no other great change in her productivity or general behavior pattern.

ONE-YEAR SUMMARY NOTE

September 15, 1960

There have been some significant changes during the last twelve-month period. Testing is still not possible. Her writing ability is definitely improved.

Lisa has continued to relate to David Green (see notes on David Green) and the relationship has become less superficial. This has apparently led to a more solidified transference to her therapist, with whom she spends more time and to whom she is more communicative. Her attention span has increased, and it is now possible to discern good orientations in time. There is less hyperactivity, giggling, and silliness. Her disassociative activity seems to be diminished. The compartmentalization of Lisa/Muriel is becoming more fluid. Though she still uses both names, Muriel comes up more frequently in the Lisa rhymes and Lisa in her Muriel printing. It is not possible to determine the degree or significance of an integrative process at this time. It should be noted, however, that on at least one occasion Lisa and Muriel became one and the patient spoke without rhyming.

Her rhyming activity has undergone a significant transition. Her rhyming two years ago consisted of nonsense syllables meaningful only to herself and was full of neologisms and clang formations. The rhymings at this time were largely primitive productions of primary process and mainly autistic formulations. At times the productions were jumbled enough to be considered a word salad not unlike that of classic hebephrenia. About a year ago her rhyming underwent a more and more pronounced change. It seldom resembled a word salad and began to make much sense. It lost much of the neologic formation and began to deal less with autistic material and more with environmental properties. In short, it changed from a primary-process phenomenon to a secondary-process one. It dealt less with her inner world and more with the outer one she lives in. Her rhymings more and more became comments on things going on about her. The third and final phase of the rhyming transition occurred during this last year and has become more developed during the last six months. This phase has largely consisted of using the rhymes to communicate—to talk to both John and David. An obviously increased desire to talk with David and her therapist has made it more difficult to rhyme. Perhaps a combination of things is taking place.

Perhaps her increased trust in herself plus the desire to talk are leading to loosening of the rhyming defense.

Despite obvious progress, the patient continues to be hyperactive, continues to rhyme, continues to be autistic at times, continues to disassociate (though diminished), and in general continues to be extremely immature. She also continues to demonstrate inappropriate affect—though not as inappropriate as on admission. She continues to be fearful, at times hiding in closets for long periods.

PROGNOSIS: In view of duration and intensity of illness, prognosis, while brighter, remains very serious.

RECOMMENDATION: Continued institutionalization and continued relating therapy.

∞

David Green

INITIAL INTAKE NOTE   *September 15, 1958*

This fifteen-year-old white boy appears to be about his stated age. Physical examination reveals a tall, thin, normally developed fifteen-year-old.

Age—15	Blood Study—Negative
Height—5' 10"	Urine Analysis—Normal
Weight—131	Chest X-ray—Normal
Blood Pressure—110/76	Skin reveals no stigmata.

Pulse—70
Respiration—Normal
Temperature—98.6

Eye—myopic, moderate.
Ears, nose, and throat are normal.
Extremities are normal.

Neurologic examination—including neuromuscular reflexes; response to light, touch, cold, heat, pain; hearing, seeing; and fundi examination—is negative.

In conclusion, there is no evidence of system pathology. Neurologic, respiratory, circulatory, digestive, and urinary examination reveals no demonstrable lesion.

PSYCHIATRIC EXAMINATION: This is a tall, small-boned, narrow-shouldered, white boy, who appears to be approximately his stated age. His hair is straight, dark blond, and perfectly parted on the side. His eyes are large, light blue, and sleepy-looking. His skin is light and clear, his mouth small, teeth even, and nose straight and fine. His features are regular and in good proportion to one another, but his face seems small for his body and has a pinched quality. David is always dressed completely and immaculately in either a gray tweed or blue serge suit, white shirt, and matching tie. His black shoes shine faultlessly, and his socks are held high by garters. He wears brown horn-rimmed glasses.

He speaks in a low, well-modulated voice, often with obvious if not blatant sarcasm, at other times with only a suggestion of sarcasm and bitterness. His pronunciation is excellent—each word being enunciated with precise clarity. His characteristic precision of speech seems to be effortless and probably a habit of long standing.

The patient is well oriented in all spheres and does not demonstrate overt evidence of hallucinating phenomena. His memory is excellent, and his vocabulary extensive. I.Q. is extremely high. The patient enters interview situations and psychologic testing reluctantly. There is sufficient co-operation, however, to glean considerable information. During interviews the patient demonstrates considerable controlled hostility which makes itself felt by sarcasm and an occasional muffled outburst of anger. Affect is appropriate for the most part. There is, however, some flattening, best demonstrated in areas where considerably less emotion is expressed than would be expected. There is enormous arrogance, and a thin veneer of superiority, undoubtedly evidence of extreme underlying fragility and fear of emotional contact. The patient had become increasingly seclusive and fearful up the time of his present admission. The latter seclusiveness and fear continue.

The patient is phobic about bodily contact. He cannot tolerate being touched. Physical examination was very difficult, David having insisted on placing the stethoscope, diaphragm, etc., himself. The latter condition has existed for at least five years and has increased in intensity in the last few months prior to entrance at this institution. At present this phobia borders on the delusional, inasmuch as the patient feels that touching may result in death.

David is obsessed with cleanliness, neatness, logic, and precision. A specific obsession involves time and time-keeping mechanisms. He spends many hours drawing clocks and watches and during interviewing expressed much preoccupation with time.

He has good abstraction ability but unexpectedly tends to become concrete intermittently. This concrete approach is mainly expressed in an attempt to mechanize much of his thinking. When he does become involved in discussion, he intellectualizes a great deal and in general impresses the examiner with much overintellectualization. He undoubtedly spends much of his time secluded and preoccupied in autistic activity. While he will discuss general issues, physics, math, clocks, time, and some philosophy, he remains detached and alienated when discussing himself, absolutely refusing to describe early memories, relationships, or his family. Attempts at such discussion result in circumstantiality and evasiveness. Despite some apparent intellectual insight as regards his condition and admission here, insight on any deeper level—that is, on an emotional level—is remarkably lacking. There are well-guarded manifestations of paranoid ideation, but no evidence of a thought disorder other than extreme fear of bodily contact and time-clock preoccupation. Attention span in contact with interviewers is only fair; therefore, a number of short interviews were used to elicit the latter material.

While the patient did permit psychologic testing, cooperation was at best limited. He was sarcastic, resentful, bored, and restless. Nevertheless, there were enough Rorschach and T.A.T. responses to permit some theoretical conclusions. He found I.Q. testing more tolerable and at times seemed involved and even interested.

I.Q. is above 145. General knowledge is extensive and characteristic of a much older individual. However, despite the great fund of general knowledge, a naivete characteristic of a much younger child is always in evidence. The patient demonstrates considerable narcissistic preoccupation and much infantile omnipotence. Identity is poor, as is self-esteem, with much evidence of fragility and a great fund of self-doubt. There is much underlying anxiety and anger, and a very poor ability to accept and to handle these. General fearfulness and preoccupation with death are evident throughout, as is fear of people and relationships of even a superficial nature. There is evidence of sexual upsurgence and an intense effort at control, repression, and denial. There is also much sexual confusion, especially as regards his own sexual identity, which is very poorly established. The patient is extremely defensive, and his defenses for the most part follow an obsessive-compulsive pattern with a definite tendency toward paranoid ideation. While responses and general ideation are not typically characteristic of schizophrenia, they are nevertheless quite florid and at times very bizarre. This is especially true when his anger is tapped. There is also evidence of considerable hopelessness and underlying depression, undoubtedly a function of much self-hate and degradation. There is an unusual degree of cynicism in one so young.

DIAGNOSTIC DISCUSSION: The patient has suffered from a multitude of neurotic symptoms during a majority of his young life. While the predominant symptomatic thread is characteristic of an obsessive compulsive neurosis, there are sufficient other symptoms (phobias, anxiety attacks) to warrant a diagnosis of neurotic reaction, chronic *mixed* type. However, there is also evidence of graver pathology. There is much basic anxiety, poor identification, especially in the sexual area, much self-hate, poor relatedness, and bizarre Rorschach responses, all of which make us think seriously of a diagnosis of pseudo-neurotic schizophrenia. In any case, we are dealing with a very fragile, anxiety-ridden, adolescent boy, who, defense-wise, is treading the line between neurosis and psychosis and who, despite great intelligence, is at present almost nonfunctional. The diagnosis of mixed neurosis with possible schizophrenic underpinnings will be retained for the time being.

PROGNOSIS: Serious.

RECOMMENDATION: The patient will be allowed as much freedom as possible and will be seen in psychotherapy, as willing, with Dr. Alan White.

SIX-MONTH INTERVAL NOTE: *March 15, 1959*

The patient remains seclusive, spending almost all of his time alone, with books. His motivation in treatment has been very poor. Instead of regular sessions, Dr. White has made himself available at any time and has spent time in the day room with him. However, David speaks to him only infrequently and for a few minutes at a time.

SIX-MONTH INTERVAL NOTE:
September 15, 1959

David has become slightly more communicative, occasionally returning the greeting of other patients and staff members.

He seems to be interested in Lisa Brent, at least superficially, observing her and trying to talk to her. He is also spending more time with Dr. White.

He is making more use of the library and day room.

ONE-YEAR SUMMARY NOTE:
September 15, 1960

At the beginning of this period David became interested in Lisa Brent on what he claimed was an intellectual, clinical basis. This apparently changed to an emotional relationship. He has spent increasing time with her, and there has been communication between them. He has even allowed himself to be touched by her on at least one occasion. He has also played chess with another patient, has become less seclusive, and spends time in the day room.

There has been at the same time increased interest in sessions with Dr. White and the establishment of a fairly strong positive transference.

In treatment it is obvious that he is emotionally involved with Lisa and has focused some of his externalizations and paranoid process on Lisa's therapist, probably a function of his jealousy and possessiveness. He has become less arrogant, less sarcastic, and less intellectualized. There is also evidence of less autistic preoccupation, with greater interest in himself in relation to Dr. White and the rest of the world. He has also begun to repress less, bringing up emotionally laden early memories. He does not speak of his family, however, and Dr. White has not pressed for such productions. Dr. White has likewise not touched any of his neurotic defenses (phobias, fears, or externalizations). David has also steered clear of sexual subjects, though his therapist feels that there are undoubtedly sexual feelings for Lisa present. His dreams have become less bizarre and less replete with anger and murder. In general, there is less fear of anger. Anger toward his doctor is now expressed with affect rather than as superior, intellectual statements. The patient seems more hopeful and, interestingly enough, has begun to ask for reassurance as to the possibility of growth and change.

Rorschach demonstrates slightly less bizarreness in the quality of the responses and somewhat less confusion as regards identity sexually. There is still considerable anxiety and anger, and a tendency toward paranoid ideation. There is still considerable infantilism and naivete.

Compulsive cleanliness, fear of body contact, and for the most part detachment from other people continue. The obsession with clocks and time persists, but to a lesser degree. Intellectualization also persists, but to a lesser degree.

PROGNOSIS: In view of obvious progress, especially as regards emotional involvement with another child and his therapist, prognosis is improved. David seems to be veering away from the borderline of schizophrenia. However, in view of long history and seriousness of illness, prognosis must still remain guarded.

RECOMMENDATION: Continued institutionalization here and treatment with Dr. White. If improvement continues, discharge from the institution and treatment with Dr. White outside may be possible in the next six months to a year. It must be remembered that David is still anxiety-ridden and many months away from the time when he will be able to become involved in the problems of his neurotic defenses, sexuality, and family relations.